Sarah BURNING

TIM RITTER

This book is based on actual events and real locations. The actual names of individuals were used whenever possible. Some conversations have been added for continuity.

All photographs are from the author's personal collection unless otherwise noted.

Publishing Coordinator – Sharon Kizziah-Holmes
Cover Design – Jaycee DeLorenzo

Paperback-Press
an imprint of A & S Publishing
A & S Holmes, Inc.

ISBN -13: 978-1-951772-99-4

Dedication

This book is lovingly dedicated to Orville, Sarah, Neil, Dewey, Virginia, and Gary. Their story will now be told…

ACKNOWLEDGMENTS

So many people helped with research for this book, and I can honestly say it would not have been possible without them. I spent many hours talking with and reading letters from my aunt LaVonne Ritter, and her often painful recollections helped lay much of the groundwork for this story. My dear friend and beloved cousin Jack Ritter welcomed me into his home for hours at a time, allowing me to pick his brain about details ranging from the design of the old farmhouse and where it sat on the property to what Dewey sounded like when he talked. And I must thank his lovely wife Kay for all the fine meals she fed me on those occasions when I invaded their home.

Very special thanks to Tim McCormack, Tammy McCormack, Joy McCroskey, Donnal Dye and the rest of the Dye family who shared their memories of Virginia, and both Tim and Joy for providing me with a plethora of photographs that I had never seen before.

Julian and Amanda Whyrick, the current owners of the land where the farmhouse once stood, allowed me on their property while conducting my research.

Many thanks to the Douglas County Herald Newspaper for opening their archives early in my research, and to the Douglas County Historical Society, particularly Marilyn Alms and Sharon Sanders, who shared details that they recalled and helped in many other ways. Thanks also to Clinkingbeard Funeral Home in Ava, for sharing their funeral records pertaining to this story.

Also, many thanks to John-Paul and Rachel Pitts for the time they spent with me, sharing their information.

Another cousin, Dennis Ritter, served as a test reader and shared details about his parents, Norman and Jerry Ritter, who figured prominently into the story. Additionally, my cousin Matt Ritter helped with details pertaining to his mother Dorothy and grandmother Ruth, both of whom also played a role in the story. My sisters, Debbie and Kathy, also became test readers, as did my dear friend Tammy Daughtrey.

Many thanks to fellow author Mira Canion for all the time spent discussing the storyline before I started writing, and my good buddy and fellow author John Cawlfield for his endless encouragement.

And last but certainly not least, my beloved wife Lisa, my biggest supporter and toughest critic, who pushed when I deserved a kick, read some awful early drafts, and encouraged and supported me to the fullest in this endeavor.

INTRODUCTION

The Fire. Those two words were always capitalized in my mind. The Fire was an event; no, it was ***The*** Event for the Ritter family. Many lives were forever changed because of The Fire.

As a child, I heard stories about The Fire, and how people I didn't know – a man named Dewey, a grandfather named Orville, and a baby – died in The Fire. And I knew that Granny, Uncle Neil, and some lady named Virginia survived it.

While I was in college and writing a lot for my own satisfaction, I mentioned to my mother once that I wanted to interview Neil some time and ask him what he remembered about The Fire.

"Don't you dare!" Mom cut me off in mid-sentence. "Don't you ever ask that man about The Fire. You know, he spent time in the psychiatric ward dealing with all that!"

And just like that, the idea was forbidden.

Over the years, however, I learned more and more about The Fire, and grew to realize many details about it were oversimplified, told by people who weren't there when it happened. For instance, the "baby" was actually an 18-month-old toddler, and his name was Gary. When I became a father, looking at my own toddler sons, the notion that Gary was just a growing little boy hit me like a brick.

I came to realize that The Fire was a life-changing event for more than just a handful of people, and that the story of it stands as a classic tale of innocence lost, and the triumph of a family who had to work hard to keep things together, all the while struggling to rise, literally, from the ashes.

Now, after six years of hard research, I have finally come to grips with the complete story. A story of redemption, a story of strength and perseverance, a story of survival.

1

October 27, 1959 – 3:30 a.m.
St. John's Hospital, Springfield, Missouri

The emergency room, normally quiet in the early morning hours, clamored with activity. Victims of an automobile accident occupied six of the ten beds, their pained moans overwhelming the ward with a constant low drone of suffering, the smell of rubbing alcohol and iodine wafting throughout the tiny exam rooms and hallways. A multitude of household accidents and falls filled the rest of the beds, causing the doctor on duty, Patrick Goodson, and the nurses to rush around in an attempt to handle the load and clear beds to make room for the other injured souls packed into the small waiting room.

The phone at the nurses' desk rang, and Mildred Hodges, the chief nurse, grew pale after answering. Hanging up the phone, she quickly scooted from room to room until she found Doctor Goodson busily putting the final stitch in the head of a little girl who fell down a flight of stairs. A five-year veteran of the night shift, Goodson earned a reputation of kindness, especially to the endless stream of children and elderly patients who filtered in and out of the emergency room.

"Doctor Goodson," Mildred whispered, to keep from alarming the child receiving stitches.

Goodson turned and looked at her, noticing she was pale, with a look of panic in her eyes.

"I'm going to let Nurse Lucy finish up with you, okay Lisa?" Dr. Goodson winked as he turned back to the little girl. "You take care of yourself and be careful on the stairs from now on."

The little girl nodded her head, and Goodson patted the side of her arm, turned and stepped out of the room to where Mildred waited.

"What is it, Mildred? You look like you've seen a ghost."

"Doctor Goodson, I just got a call. We have four burn victims coming from a house fire near Ava. They'll be here in a little over an hour. One of them has multiple injuries and is three months pregnant. When this little girl clears out, this will be the only room available."

"Jesus," Patrick sighed, rubbing his eyes. "Those six people from the accident aren't moving, at least not for the next few hours till we can get them stabilized. The waiting room is full, so I've got to keep moving people through as much as possible. What is the status of the other three coming?"

"The Douglas County Sheriff only said that they were burn victims. He didn't say how badly. There may not be much we can do. We may just have to assess their situation when they get here," Mildred shrugged.

"Okay, let's get this room cleaned up once Lucy finishes bandaging up the little girl. Hold it clear for the pregnant burn victim. We will figure out what to do with the other three when they get here and we get a firm grip on their conditions. Who is the OB on call?"

"Ferguson is on call tonight, I believe."

"Get him in here. If she's three months pregnant and injured, I'm going to need his expertise."

As Mildred walked quickly back to the nurses' station, Goodson surveyed the ward, trying to figure out how to make some space for more people. He looked down at his watch.

"About an hour till all hell breaks loose," he muttered to himself quietly, rubbing his eyes again. "Burn victims. What the hell am I going to do with burn victims? If it's bad, they won't last two days."

3:30 a.m.
Western Douglas County, Missouri

The still of the cold night was broken by the wail of sirens as two ambulances sped together along Highway 14, followed closely by a station wagon. The road, a twisty, bumpy two-lane, hindered the motorcade from traveling at its preferred high rate of speed. Lyle Clinkingbeard drove the lead ambulance faster than he usually dared through the twisting hillside curves in the dark road. Slowing at times to 30 miles per hour on the tighter curves, he floored the gas pedal any time he had a straightaway, flying through the towns of Sparta and Ozark in hopes of gaining time and expediting the delivery of the pained souls within the vehicles. Just before leaving the site of the fire, Lyle's father, Clarence, who was the Douglas County Coroner, owner of Clinkingbeard Funeral Home and the Clinkingbeard Ambulance Service, pulled Lyle close and whispered in his ear, "Son, these people are our friends and they are hurt really bad. Drive like the devil himself is chasing you."

In the back of Lyle's ambulance, 21-year-old Virginia Ritter faded in and out of consciousness, moaning and crying while holding her lower abdomen. Every bump in the road sent lightning bolts of pain through her broken and burned body. Lying next to her, Neil Ritter, 19, thrashed about, his blackened hands covering his seared face as he screamed repeatedly.

"Dewey! Oh God, Dewey! I tried to save you! I tried, I swear to God I tried!"

Charles Fish, driving the second ambulance, stayed closely behind Lyle, keeping an eye on his rear-view mirror to check on his burned, agonizing cargo. Sarah Ritter, 59, coughed occasionally to combat the smoke that had settled in her lungs, tears rolling down her cheeks as she sobbed. Charles called back to her along the way, in hopes of keeping her spirits up.

"Hang in there, Mrs. Ritter. We're going to get all of you to Springfield quick as a wink. You just rest back there and let ole Charlie get you to the hospital."

"Thank you, dear," answered the weak quivering voice in the back.

George Pledger's station wagon sped along behind the second ambulance. George drove in silence while in the back, Sarah's 60-

year-old husband, Orville, lay on a pile of blankets that Carrie Pledger had gathered. Orville struggled to breathe as the car sped through the darkness. A large man with a big barrel chest, he didn't rest well on his back under normal circumstances. Now, badly burned and lungs filled with smoke, he struggled to breathe and remain conscious.

2

The Ritter farmhouse sat near the edge of a steep bluff on forty acres of wooded rolling hills on Hunter Road, a rocky dirt road barely wide enough for two horse-drawn carts to pass, that twisted and snaked down into the Turkey Creek valley about four miles east of Ava, Missouri. Built in 1932, the four-room house was little more than a drafty shack when Orville Ritter and his wife Sarah purchased the property and moved in with their eight children in September 1939. With the youngest sons, twins Delmas and Delbert barely six months old and 39-year-old Sarah beginning to feel the effects of child number nine on the way, the family considered the house and its electrical wiring a vast improvement over anything else in which they had lived.

The family settled in before the onset of winter and enjoyed their large, albeit drafty, new home. Orville and Sarah set up their bed in the first-floor living room. On the second level, above the living room, the girls commandeered the north bedroom, the only room upstairs with its own door, offering some much-needed privacy. The boys crammed into two beds in the south bedroom, over the kitchen. The narrow stairs leading to the upper level, treacherous at best, required great caution going up or down. The tread, only about six inches deep, required anyone ascending or descending to walk sideways. Orville vowed to rework them some day when they could afford it.

The spring of 1940 brought abundance upon the family, as Orville discovered the ground to be more fertile than he originally expected. In a flat area below the bluff over which the house sat, about an acre of rich soil became one of Orville's best garden spots. Carved from a river that flowed through the area thousands of years before, the little piece of land sported a freshwater spring that fed down the hill to the river, and more importantly provided plenty of water for the family.

On May 16 of that year, another son, Dallas Neil, entered the world, and Orville and Sarah agreed that nine children was enough. The family thrived in their new home, with good crops and the addition of livestock grazing on some of the acreage. The house, typically bustling with activity, became a common location for family gatherings. Orville's brother Richard, with whom he was quite close, visited often with his wife Cora and children Norma Rea and Jack. In addition, Orville's only sister, Dora, showed up from time to time with her ornery husband, Glen "Pete" Franklin.

In August of 1944, the first Ritter child left the household. Norman, who had grown into a tall, strong 18-year-old with a husky voice that betrayed his youth, enlisted in the Army and by February 1945 found himself on German soil as part of the 9th Army. A piece of shrapnel from a German 88-millimeter artillery shell took him out of action for five weeks with a shoulder wound, and he was released from the hospital in Belgium on May 13, 1945, five days after the German surrender (VE Day). Norman spent the rest of his Army time serving in the occupation force until his discharge in mid-1946. Once again a civilian, Norman returned to Ava and began working as a mechanic for the Kester Sales Company, a car dealership in town. He also dated and married Wanda Jirleen "Jerry" Woods, the sister of one of his childhood friends. After marrying on October 16, 1947, in Mountain Home, Arkansas, Norman and Jerry lived in Ava, then eventually moved to Springfield, Missouri, an hour away from Ava, where Norman began working at the newly opened Kraft Foods plant in their maintenance department.

Through the 1940s and into the 1950s, the old farmhouse suffered, becoming draftier as the outer shell of rough-hewn boards deteriorated from the effects of the seasons. During cold weather months, the wood stove had to run hotter to combat the drafts that chilled everyone inside. The children slept fully clothed with several blankets and quilts piled on them while little heat found its way to the upstairs bedrooms. Spring and fall rains brought leaks, which meant pots, pans and buckets scattered about the floors upstairs, in hopes of catching the rainwater before it seeped through the upper floor into the living room or kitchen below.

As his children got older, Orville's health also began to suffer. Arthritis affected nearly every joint, especially his hands. Additionally, he reportedly suffered from a heart ailment. Years of smoking unfiltered cigarettes left his voice gravelly and deep, and he typically spoke in short bursts. Forced to give up most of his farming by the mid-1950s, he sold all his cattle, renting out a majority of his pasture to neighboring farmers. His prized garden area became overgrown with weeds and briars from neglect, causing Sarah to create a small garden that was easier to access across the driveway.

With the money gained from the cattle sale, the house received a much-needed upgrade. A new roof ended the leaking issue, and asphalt sheet siding was added to the outside of the house. Patterned to look like bricks, the siding greatly improved the overall appearance of the house. The rickety old staircase was rebuilt as well, though due to space restrictions, it remained steep and treacherous. Sarah beamed over the improvements and applied a new layer of wallpaper to the walls and ceilings throughout the house.

In 1953 while a junior in high school, middle son Dewey developed an interest in electronics and began working for local TV and radio repair services, including Ava Radio and Electric Company. Soon he had his own repair business, operating in the back of Marshall Auto Store. Like his older brother Norman, Dewey stood out in a crowd. Extremely handsome with black hair and brown eyes, he was smart, strong, outgoing, with a genuinely pleasant disposition, which served him well in his interactions with his local customers, often rural folks who needed help tuning a radio or setting the antenna for a television set.

May 1954 witnessed Dewey graduating high school, after which he signed up to join the Air Force. Telling his cousin Jack about his plans one night while they drove around town, Dewey beamed about the possibilities.

"You're such a good shot with a rifle, better than anyone I've ever seen," Jack grinned. "I'm surprised you decided to go into the Air Force instead of the Army."

"Yeah, but it's all about electronics, Jack," Dewey announced proudly. "Man, electronics is going to be the wave of the future. And the Air Force is going to teach me more than I could ever learn here. Then I'm going to come home and marry Virginia Dye while I'm on leave."

"Virginia Dye?" Jack looked at Dewey. "What happened to that other girl, what's her name?"

"Don't even say it!" Dewey laughed. "No way. Virginia and I have been sparkin' for quite some time, and I really like her. She's something special. I'm going to marry her, just you watch!"

Pretty little Virginia Dye, two years younger than Dewey, came from another family who, like the Ritters, resided in Douglas County for many generations. She quietly fell in love with Dewey from afar several years before they started dating. By 1954 however, their relationship was a matter of official record. She is noted as an attendee at the funeral when Orville's mother died in July of 1954. Additionally, in the local news section of the Douglas County Herald on July 15 of that same year, Virginia was the sole guest listed at a Ritter family dinner held at Norman's house. After many years of loving him from a distance, Virginia finally had her man.

On Christmas Day of 1955, Norman and Jerry came to visit the Ava folks with their son, 4-year-old Dennis. They brought special news with them.

"Jerry and I want to give you both something special for Christmas this year."

"What's on your mind, son?" Sarah furrowed her brow, settling down on the arm of Orville's chair, her arm around his back as he rested his arm on her leg.

"We know times are tough, and we want to give you something you've always wanted."

Orville and Sarah stared blankly at them.

Norman grinned.

"A front porch."

"What?" Orville blurted out.

"Yeah, Dad. I know you've always wanted a front porch," Norman explained as Jerry grinned at Sarah. "That rotten old thing out front needs to go. You deserve a nice concrete porch with an eave over it. So Jerry and I are buying the materials, and we're going to come down here in the spring, and we're going to build you a porch."

"Lot of money, Norman" Orville scowled.

"Don't you worry about it, Dad," Norman stood up. "This is something we want to do."

"Okay Norman!" Orville laughed, reaching up to shake Norman's hand as Sarah got up and walked over to Jerry to hug her.

In early March, with the trees still bare and a chill lingering in the Turkey Creek valley, two trucks pulled into Orville and Sarah's driveway, hauling lumber and material for the upgrade. Orville stepped out of the house when he heard the trucks and directed them to unload behind the house. Ray, who happened to be visiting that day, stepped out to the back of the house to stand with Orville to watch the process of unloading and stacking the lumber. After a brief silence, Ray couldn't resist making a suggestion.

"You know, Dad, I hear that all of Hunter Road is getting hooked up with telephones. It's called a farm line and will be hooked up so that all of us on Hunter Road can talk to each other. Might be something good to add while we're getting all this work done."

Orville shot him a look, then went back to watching the workers. After a long silence, he took in a deep breath.

"Ray, after all this… all this work is done, you suppose the neighbors will no longer come visit?"

"I don't think that at all, Dad." Ray shrugged.

"You think… we won't walk up the road, visit our neighbors no more?"

"No, I can't see that happening either." Ray shrugged again.

Orville slowly lit a cigarette.

"Then why would I want more wires run to my house… to talk to my neighbors… without seeing them? No sir. Don't want no part of it."

He began gesturing with his cigarette between his fingers.

"Neighbors should visit neighbors. Not rely on some electrical de-vice to do their visiting for them. No, son, I don't think so. Not at this house."

The subject of a telephone was never brought up again.

Work began in April on the new porch. The old rock and stone structure fell victim to a sledgehammer and was broken up to provide foundation and fill for the new concrete that ran nearly the entire width of the house. An eave, attached just under the front ventilation windows for the upstairs bedrooms, covered the entire porch with shade, supported by several wood columns which had been sunk into the concrete for stability. All the windows received new trim, and the entire rock foundation under the house was sealed with concrete.

After the last nail was driven into the front window trim, Norman and Orville stood in the front yard, staring at the beautiful home. Orville, not saying a word, looked everything over, rubbing his face with his hands. He looked up and down, to the left then the right, then up and down again. Norman watched his dad survey the work.

Orville then walked around the back of the house, ran his hand along the door trim, then stepped back to get a better look at that side of the house. Norman stood next to him, grinning, trying to figure out which details his silent father was studying as they strolled.

Orville then walked to the north of the house, with Norman still in tow, then walked again to the front of the house, studying everything all over again.

Finally Orville took a deep breath.

"Looks really good, Norman. No words to thank you enough. Really looks wonderful. Your mom's pleased too."

"I'm sure glad, Dad. This is something we wanted to do for you guys," Norman patted his dad on the back.

"Thank you, Norman. Thank you."

That night, Orville watched the sun set over the hills from his new front porch.

The summer and fall of 1956 saw the farmhouse filled with excitement. Several of the Ritter kids experienced big changes.

The twins Delbert and Delmas, who grew up singing together, spent their spare time playing guitars and performing around the area. The boys were discovered by Loyd Evans, radio personality and promoter on KGBX radio in Springfield, when his *Country Caravan* program travelled to Ava in July. With the promise of making them stars, Evans offered to let the boys move to his home in Springfield, where his wife Ravay enrolled the boys in newly built Parkview High School. Thus the twins began living the life of musicians an hour away in Springfield.

At the end of August, the oldest daughter, Wanda, married George "Speedy" Bollinger, a tall, broad-shouldered guy with a soft heart and kind temperament. Speedy ran a storefront on the public square in Seymour, Missouri, which served as a small grocery and café. Rather than deal with the hubbub that normally accompanies planning a wedding, Wanda and Speedy decided to get married at the courthouse without telling anyone, then broke the news to everyone. Both families, already taken with the couple, happily accepted the news and welcomed the union.

The other excitement was the news that Dewey planned to come home in late October after completing a 32-week training course in radar technician school at Kessler Air Force Base in Biloxi, Mississippi. In a letter sent just after Wanda's wedding, Dewey informed his parents that he would be home on the 29th and that he planned to stay three weeks before he had to report to his next assignment, which was to be a nearly three-year stint at Orly Air Force Base in Paris, France.

His parents didn't know, however, that he also called Virginia Dye the same day he sent the letter.

"Hey sweetheart! How's my girl?"

"I'm okay. Oh, Dewey, I miss you so much."

"I miss you too, baby. I don't have much time, so I need to tell you I just got my orders."

"Oh? Where will you be stationed?"

"Well, let me put it this way… have you ever wanted to see Paris?"

"Paris, Texas? I didn't think they had a base there."

"No silly, Paris, France," Dewey laughed.

"Paris, France? You mean like the real Paris? You mean… you mean, you are going to be stationed overseas in Paris, France?"

"Yes, love. *We* are going to live in Paris, France. I've been ordered to be stationed at Orly Air Force Base there. We are going to move there."

"What did you say? We?" Virginia got quiet.

"Come on, honey! Let's get married! I'm going to have three weeks leave to collect things, and I applied to bring you over with me. I'm coming home at the end of October. We can get married, and I can set up a place for us to live in Paris. Then when the paperwork comes through, you can come live there too!"

"Dewey… did… did you just propose to me?"

"Yes, honey. You know I love you. I'd get down on one knee but I don't think you can see me from there. I love you, Virginia Dye. I'd like for you to become Virginia Ritter, please. Will you marry me?"

"Yes. Yes, of course, Dewey! You know I've loved you for years. Oh but, Dewey…" Virginia's voice lowered. "What about Daddy? Don't you want to ask his permission? I mean, it's only proper to do that."

"Ha! I've already talked to him!" Dewey laughed. "I called earlier and we had a nice man-to-man talk. I told him how much I love you, what my situation here is, and where we are going. I promised him that I would take good care of you, always put you first in my life, and love you till my dying breath."

"What?" Virginia didn't know whether to be happy with Dewey or mad at her dad for keeping a secret.

"Yep! He said, 'Dewey, I've grown to love you like my own son. And I know Virginia loves you, too. That's my little girl, you know. But you most certainly have my permission, on one condition. You wait till after she turns 18.'"

"Really!"

"Yep! So here's the deal: I'm getting out of here on the 27th and I'll drive to Ava that day and spend the night at Mom and Dad's. Then we'll get married on the 31st…"

"Dewey, that's Halloween!" Virginia laughed.

"Yeah, silly, we'll get married on Halloween! How 'bout it?"

"Okay! Let's do it!" Virginia squealed.

"Great! So we will get married on the 31st. See if Reverend Duffer can marry us. We can have a honeymoon there in Ava and enjoy hanging around for a bit before I have to leave."

Tears welled up in Virginia's eyes.

"Oh, Dewey. I'm so happy! I can't wait to be your wife."

Everything went as planned. Dewey asked Norman and Jerry to stand with them during the wedding, and in a simple ceremony in the living room of Reverend Duffer's parsonage, Dewey and Virginia exchanged vows. Time passed quickly for the newlyweds, who took up temporary residence in Virginia's bedroom at the home of her parents, Garland and Lula Dye, who lived just a few miles from the Ritters east of Ava.

The day of Dewey's departure was tearful, to say the least. But time passed quickly, the paperwork was approved, and by June of 1957, Virginia was set to join Dewey in France. After packing a couple of suitcases, Virginia had her dad drive her over to the Ritter farmhouse to say goodbye to Orville and Sarah. After a brief visit, Virginia found herself boarding an airplane in Springfield to fly to St. Louis, then on to New York, then Paris.

Things turned unexpectedly difficult at the Ritter home in the weeks and months after Virginia left for Paris. Neil, set to graduate high school in the spring of 1958, failed his art class in the last semester of his senior year, so graduation was denied him. Angry to have failed, Neil refused to enroll that fall to retake the class to graduate. Instead, he spent his time staying at Norman's house in Springfield to look for a job.

Good news arrived from Paris in May of 1958, as Virginia gave birth to a healthy baby boy, named Gary Landon Ritter. A little card arrived at each Ritter and Dye home, announcing the birth. The entire family, expectedly overjoyed, looked forward to the return of the growing young family in late 1959.

The first months of 1959 were brutally difficult in the old farmhouse on Hunter Road. The winter was particularly harsh, with repeated snowstorms and exceptionally cold temperatures. The daily chore of hauling water to the house from the spring was treacherous at best, and in the snow and ice it became dangerous.

By early fall, the twins were no longer living with Loyd Evans, receiving mail at Norman's house, as Sarah's letter from September 29th was sent to the twins in care of Norman's address. The letter mentioned that Dewey, Virginia, and little Gary would be home soon. They were scheduled to arrive in New York on October 14th and would stay there for a day or two to wrap up discharge papers and make arrangements to get home to Ava.

Sometime in early October, the twins pulled into the Carriage House truck stop and restaurant in Springfield. There, they caught the eyes of two waitresses, Mary Moore and Dorothy Moody. Soon the four were going out on double dates almost nightly.

Life on the farm had taken an unfortunate twist by October. With Orville's health declining, including reduced energy from heart issues, and progression of his rheumatoid arthritis, his ability to carry water to the house from the nearby spring was pretty much over. Sarah, also suffering from arthritis and the ravages of time, struggled to carry water as well. Sarah's letters to the twins reflected her frustration with her inability to carry the water and advised the twins of each time one of the sons or sons-in-law helped them by carrying multiple buckets of water to the house.

According to the letters, Orville contemplated selling the house, presumably to move into town to a house with running water but knew that they would have to dig a well to make the old farmhouse more marketable. Their income, meager at best, was only supplemented by Orville's monthly disability check for $60.

Further complicating the monetary situation, Orville and Sarah took out a loan at the bank in Ava to give money to the twins for the purchase of a car, which they needed to get to music gigs, as well as to drive to job inquiries. The loan put an additional financial strain on the farmhouse budget, and Sarah's letters between April and October of 1959 implored the boys to do whatever they could to pay her back. In the October letter, she gave them a deadline of the 21st to come up with some money or sell their car. It was the only such ultimatum given in any of the letters.

"The people at the bank were very nice this morning when I asked for more time," Sarah wrote of her humbling visit.

Neil left Norman's house in Springfield and returned to the farmhouse in Ava in early October to look for a job locally, and to help with the upkeep of the house, including the ever-present need to carry water from the spring. In her October letter, Sarah mentioned Neil and the fact that he was going to help Jack Ritter take some young calves to the auction for Orville's brother-in-law

Glen "Pete" Franklin.

Dewey, Virginia, and little Gary landed in New York according to plan on Wednesday, October 14th. Lugging all of their belongings and their necessities for Gary, the young family made it to a hotel just in time to collapse and fall asleep around midnight. Dewey had an appointment with the Air Force office at 10:00 the next morning, so fortunately the family got to sleep a little later than normal. They enjoyed breakfast together in their room before Dewey's departure for his appointment. By the end of the day, his discharge from the Air Force completed and remaining pay received, he was a free man. The family celebrated that night with a nice dinner, again in their room.

Friday, October 15th, Dewey made flight arrangements to get the family home to Ava. From New York, they were to fly to St. Louis on TWA, then catch an Ozark Air Lines flight to Springfield. Garland and Lula Dye promised to pick them up at the Springfield airport, then drive them back to Ava, to stay with the Dyes for several days before moving to the Ritter farmhouse on October 26th. Orville and Sarah made plans to have all the family come to the house on Saturday, October 31st, which would be Dewey and Virginia's third wedding anniversary, and would be the perfect day for a big family dinner to welcome back the airman and his brood.

October 26, 1959
Orville and Sarah Ritter's farmhouse near Ava, Missouri

With their time at the Dye house completed as planned, Dewey and Virginia packed up Gary and all their belongings to move for a few days to the Ritter farm. Garland drove them the few miles to the old house on Hunter Road. It was Dewey's first time back in three years, and he and Virginia savored every moment watching the grandparents enjoy playing with Gary, who, born while Dewey was stationed in Paris, was getting to know the Ritters for the first time.

And there was news to share…

"So, Mom, you seem to be enjoying little Gary quite a bit!" Dewey chuckled as he and Virginia watched his mother crawl around on the floor of the living room, rolling a ball back and forth with Gary.

"Oh, honey, you know how I feel about all these grandkids." Sarah grinned as she looked over her shoulder, then back to Gary. "Granny just wants to eat them up!" she cackled in a high-pitched voice.

"Never seen anything like it, that woman with young'uns," Orville shook his head and laughed from his chair across the room.

"Well that's good," Dewey grabbed Virginia's hand and looked at her, winking, "because you might want to think about looking over here," as he put his hand on Virginia's stomach.

Sarah's eyes widened.

"How about another baby in this family?" Virginia smiled, resting her hand over Dewey's, still on her stomach.

"Are you in a family way, honey?" Sarah got up quickly.

"Mama, she's three months along!" Dewey gloated.

"Hallelujah!" Sarah threw her hands up as Orville jumped up out of his chair, yelling "Hey!"

Sarah ran over and hugged Virginia while Dewey got up and shook hands with his dad. A flurry of conversation ensued, the ladies discussing when Virginia started feeling something, whether she had any morning sickness, and if it was planned. Dewey and Orville didn't talk nearly as much, and after a brief conversation just stood and smiled as the ladies continued to talk.

Just then Neil walked in with a load of firewood.

"What in sam hell was all that yelling about?" he asked playfully with a grin.

"Virginia's gonna have another pup!" Orville laughed, pointing at the ladies.

"Well I'll be! You know I've heard they finally figured out what causes that." Neil laughed as he leaned in and gave Dewey a big hug. "I'm happy for you, big brother. That's great news."

Later, with full bellies from a celebratory dinner, the family settled into a night filled with stories and laughter in the living room, around the roaring wood stove. The temperature outside dropped into the upper thirties as a cold wind began to blow from the north. Neil earlier stacked a pile of wood on the front porch, with a big load dumped in the living room by the front door.

Just before 8:00, the family heard a car pulling in the driveway.

Once it stopped near the house, the horn honked as Neil put his coat on.

"That's Jack," Neil said, fumbling with his buttons. "We're going to run around town for a bit. Wanna go, Dewey?"

"No, I think I'll pass. Thanks though, Neil." Dewey looked up as he bounced Gary on his knee. "I ran around with Jack for a while earlier today to catch up. Tell him I'll see him this weekend."

"You got it."

"Check the wood stove when you get home, son," Orville called out as Neil ran out the door. "It's gonna be a cold night!"

At about 9:00, Sarah and Virginia walked through the kitchen just as Dewey plugged in the electric coffee pot.

"I guess you boys are staying up?" Virginia asked as she held Gary, who was sleepily rubbing his eyes, "Mom and I are headed upstairs to put Gary to bed."

"Yeah baby," Dewey said, kissing her on the cheek. "Dad and I are going to stay up a bit and have another cup of coffee before bed. I won't be too long. Goodnight buddy." Dewey kissed Gary's forehead. "Daddy loves his little man."

As Virginia made her way to the stairs with Gary, Sarah stepped up and smothered Dewey with another hug.

"Sure glad to have you home, son," Sarah said softly, leaning up to kiss Dewey's cheek.

"Thanks, Mom. It's nice to be home. Looking forward to being here a few days. Thanks for giving us the room up there."

"Hope you all sleep well in there, dear." Sarah smiled as she turned to climb the stairs.

Within an hour, Dewey and Orville finished their coffee, stoked the wood stove, and headed upstairs for bed.

The north wind still blew relentlessly at midnight when Jack dropped off Neil in the driveway. Once inside, Neil checked the wood stove, as promised. Adding a couple of logs, he made sure the air vent was half open, then walked through the dark kitchen and quietly climbed the stairs to the second floor.

Before stepping into the north bedroom where his parents slept, Neil paused for a moment and looked at Dewey and Virginia sleeping soundly, then heard little Gary quietly snore from the crib near the foot of the bed. Smiling, Neil stepped into the north bedroom and closed the door. Undressing quietly, he crammed his five-foot-nine-inch frame into the small twin bed, covered up, and quickly fell asleep.

As Neil settled into a restful slumber, smoke from an unknown source began to waft through the first floor.

3

October 27, 2:28 a.m.
Ritter Farmhouse, near Ava, Missouri

Neil stirred.

Rolling from his back to his right side, in the midst of his sleep, he smelled smoke. It wasn't the familiar aroma of cigarette smoke, nor the smell of a campfire. In his dreamy, vision-cluttered mind, the smell triggered the memory of a day, not so many years prior, when he and his brothers were in the hay barn, playing with matches.

Neil smiled in his sleep, remembering how he and Delbert and Delmas scampered up the rickety ladder into the hay loft, laughing and playing grab-ass all the way. Sitting down on the hay bales left from the last time they were there, they each lit a cigarette. In its dreamy state, Neil's mind remembered lighting a match and dropping it on the hay, and how Delbert and Delmas scampered to put it out quickly. As the game progressed, Neil threw more matches onto the hay, and the twins worked more quickly to stamp them out.

Neil grunted in his sleep as he recalled one match that didn't get stamped out, and a small fire developed. Not a good situation in a barn filled with hay intended to last throughout the winter, the boys scrambled to extinguish the quickly spreading fire. Growing taller, the flames spread toward a large stack along the rear wall. Wishing they had some water, the boys worked feverishly.

"Neil, help me!" cried Delbert, his foot beginning to burn while he stamped on the flames.

Feeling confident that he had his spot stamped out, Neil ran over and helped subdue the fire as it began to encircle Delbert.

"You threw the matches out too damn fast, Neil!" Delmas yelped, hoping to throw the blame on his younger brother.

"You wanted me to!" Neil snapped back as Delmas glared at him.

"Come on guys, let's just get this fire out," Delbert growled, and within a few moments of stamping and sweeping away unburnt hay, the fire was finally out.

"We won't tell anyone this happened, right?" Delmas panted, looking at his brothers, leaning over from being so winded.

"Right," both answered.

The smell of burnt hay lingered in the loft as the boys caught their breath.

In his dreamy state, Neil took another breath, drawing in another smell of smoke. Not the smell of burning hay. More like the smell of burning wallpaper.

He rolled over onto his back, his mind drifting off to that icy winter day as he sat in the living room. A cold, biting north wind rattled the window next to him, causing him to shift on the couch next to Delbert. The two boys looked up at the ceiling, their attention drawn to a glow near the exposed chimney brick. Neil frowned. The stove was burning too hot.

Near the chimney, the wallpaper on the ceiling caught fire. A thin line, glowing orange, slithered across the surface like a sidewinder rattlesnake, leaving behind singed remnants of the previous layers of wallpaper and exposed ceiling boards.

His brow furrowed in his sleep.

Neil took another breath.

Once again he smelled smoke. Not the smell of burning hay. Not the smell of burning wallpaper. Not the familiar delicious smell of a newly lit cigarette. Not even the smell of a campfire.

Lumber... Lumber burning... Wood... Wood burning... Wood on fire... Fire... Something is on fire...

Neil's eyes popped open.

Sitting up straight in his bed and shaking his head to gather his wits, Neil ran his fingers through his hair and blinked twice to focus his eyes. He looked around the room, hearing his parents snoring in the bed nearby. Still trying to awaken, he noticed a faint orange glow showing in the cracks of the floorboards, and a stronger orange light from the staircase. The acrid smell of burning wood filled the room, reminding him of countless bonfires.

At once, he became aware of an ominous low roar that seemed to come from everywhere within the house.

What the hell is that roar...sounds like a damn train comin'. Guess I'd better go down and check on the wood stove.

Neil tossed aside the old quilt he slept under and got out of bed.

Why is the floor so damn hot?

Hearing a slight crackling noise, Neil turned his head left. Through the bedroom doorway, he could see the top of the rickety old staircase. The orange glow from downstairs was bright.

Then he saw it.

It only lasted a moment. Then, in an instant, there was another. And another.

Flames.

Neil drew in a deep breath.

"Fire!"

He screamed as loud as he could and ran into Dewey and Virginia's room.

"Mom! Dad! Dewey! Virginia! Everybody get up! The house is on fire!"

Neil looked down the narrow wooden staircase, cringing as the heat from the floor burned his bare feet.

If we can get down these stairs, we could be out the back door in seconds...

The flames on the staircase sneered back at Neil, mocking him. The flames danced higher and glowed brighter, showing him that each step was on fire, and had been for some time. They'd burn alive trying to get down the stairs, or worse, fall through the stairs and land below in the cellar.

Oh my God. There's no way.

"We have to jump! The stairs are on fire!" he screamed.

The flames leapt up the walls and began to slip through cracks in the floor. Smoke billowed, thick and black, and everyone began to cough as the yelling woke them up.

Dewey learned two things during his service in the Air Force: how to eat quickly, and how to wake up quickly. Drills to fight fires or prepare for attacks occurred randomly, and often the alarm sounded in the middle of the night, requiring immediate clarity and quick action. The first two times it happened, he found it difficult to wake up. The ass-chewing he received from his sergeant afterwards cured him of his difficulty. He learned that waking up quickly and clearly would alleviate such unpleasantness. Dewey's quick-waking instincts kicked in with the sound of Neil screaming.

"Neil! You jump out of the window in there first then catch Mom and then Dad!" Dewey yelled, jumping out of bed. "Virginia and I will jump from here! Go!"

Neil turned and ran back into the north bedroom, as Orville and Sarah jumped out of bed. Stepping on the hot floor in her bare feet, Sarah screamed.

"Oh dear God, it's hot! We haven't much time!"

Not stopping to put on pants or a shirt, Neil ran over to the window.

"Gotta bust out that window, son," Orville yelled, letting out a cough.

"Dear Jesus, help us!" Sarah put her hands to her face as Neil grabbed the old chair by his bed and busted the window open. With their stocky build, neither Sarah nor Orville could jump with just the bottom pane slid open, so the whole window had to be gone for escape. As the window shattered, a blast of cold air blew in and rushed down the stairs, adding more fuel to the hungry fire, which by now engulfed everything on the first level, shooting easily up through the hollow walls to consume the second floor. The entire house began to ominously moan and creak. Flames leapt up through the cracks in the hot floor, the walls bursting into flames as everyone began to burn. Sarah ran to Orville's side and held on to him tightly.

Neil stood at the open window and turned back to his parents, yelling to be heard over the roar.

"I'm going to jump, then I want you to jump, Mom! Then you, Dad! I'll catch you!"

Ignoring the possibility of glass fragments below, Neil jumped, landing in the damp cold grass with a quick roll to absorb the impact. Standing up, chilled in the cold wind, he turned and stepped quickly underneath the window, his mother watching from the burning window frame.

As Neil sprinted back into the north bedroom after awakening everyone, Virginia jumped up and ran around to the foot of the bed to grab Gary, who had been sleeping in a crib they brought from Virginia's parents' house. Now standing in his crib and screaming from being awakened so suddenly, he stood with his arms outstretched as his mother leaned over and picked him up.

The big iron-framed bed in which Dewey and Virginia had moments before slept soundly was positioned in the middle of the south wall, partially blocking the window. Now that the window was their only means of escape, the iron bed needed to move. Dewey put all his weight into the side of the heavy iron frame to shove it away from the window. Flames crawled up the walls and slipped between the cracks in the floorboards, causing Virginia to jump and yell with fright, adding to Gary's high-pitched screaming. Both barefoot, Dewey and Virginia tried to step lightly, the flames burning their feet. Virginia held Gary with one arm, all the while cradling her stomach with the other.

"Oh my God, Dewey!" Virginia yelled repeatedly.

As she stood holding Gary and her stomach, the crib behind her, where Gary had slept only moments before, burst into flames.

The fire, now consuming the walls of the second level and spreading across the ceiling, roared and crackled, searing everyone with its heat. The dresser to Sarah's left burst into flames, the antique mirror exploding, sending shards of glass into the room. Standing there at the window in her bare feet, dressed in only a nightgown, she had to keep her burning feet moving. Her nightgown began to smoke. Orville stood behind her, also shifting his weight from foot to foot, clad only in his underwear. The entire house roared.

"Mom! Jump!" screamed Neil from outside below the window.

"C'mon, Mother. You gotta jump." Orville moved Sarah closer to the window, his hands around her waist.

"I'm so scared, Orville," she yelled, stepping to the window.

"Honey, please jump as soon as I'm on the ground, okay?"

"Be right behind you, Mother! Now Go!" Orville shouted, hoping she heard him over the roar of the fire.

Sarah grasped the burning window frame for a moment to steady herself. The flames dancing up the walls licked at her arms and legs and glass shards in the window frame imbedded in her skin as she gathered her courage for a split second, then jumped. Though she easily outweighed Neil by at least fifty pounds, he caught her standing up, and quickly steadied her as she struggled to her feet.

Gathering her wits after the jump, she turned, standing next to Neil.

"Dad! Jump!" Neil screamed.

"Come on, Honey! Jump! Neil will catch you!" Sarah joined in.

Once Dewey got the bed out of the way, he threw his clothes off of the nearby chair, and used it to smash the window so that they could jump. The chair broke as he hit it against the window frame, so he tossed the remains of the chair aside and kicked the window frame, pushing the lower pane out and breaking the upper pane. He hit the upper pane with his hands to push out the last of the glass, turning it red as his hands were cut by the glass shards still imbedded in the wood. Turning back to Virginia, he saw the panic in her eyes. He looked at Gary, who still had his arms stretched out toward Dewey and was screaming, "Daddy!"

"Oh my God, Dewey, we're going to die!" screamed Virginia, panicking as she looked around, the flames crawling up the walls and through the floorboards. The old house continued making ominous creaking noises as the main structure began to give way. "Dewey, my baby! How are we going to get out of here? How can I jump and not hurt this baby?"

The bed burst into flames as Dewey looked at Virginia, terrified with tears rolling down her face. Gary continued stretching his arms out to Dewey, crying "Daddy!"

Orville, standing behind Sarah and watching her jump, continued shifting his weight as his feet burned. The bed, where only moments earlier they had been sleeping, stood engulfed in flames. The burning ceiling sent little orbs of fire dripping down onto everything, including Orville. The heat seared his skin while he looked down at Neil and Sarah, who were in turn looking up at him. Surrounded by flames, Orville moved closer to the window.

"Come on, Dad! Jump!"

Coughing, Orville grabbed the burning window frame and prepared to jump.

Then he stopped and looked up through the smoke into the sky.

No, I can't jump like this. I need to put some pants on. I'm just in my underwear. What would the neighbors think?

He backed away from the window, and carefully walked over to the chair by the bedroom door, coughing and gagging on the thick black smoke filling the room as Neil and Sarah screamed at him from outside. Feeling around in the dark, he found his overalls. Through the roar of the flames, he could hear yelling and screaming coming from the next room where Dewey, Virginia and Gary had been sleeping. He couldn't see anything through the thick smoke, but he heard the distinct sound of his grandson crying and repeatedly screaming, "Daddy!"

"Virginia, honey, we're not going to die! It's all going to be okay! Roll when you hit the ground and the baby will be fine! It's an old Air Force trick. Remember, roll when you hit the ground," yelled Dewey, trying to be heard over the roar of the flames and constant screaming, as Gary was terrified and burning from the heat in the room. "You're going to have to jump first. Try to land as close to the house as you can so that you don't go down the gulley. Then I'll toss Gary down to you. Then I'll jump and we'll run around to the front of the house. When you land, get up as soon as you can so that you can catch Gary. Okay?"

Virginia handed Gary to Dewey and turned to the open window to jump. She grabbed the burning window frame and looked down at the small six-foot-wide patch of ground below, then past the big sycamore tree outside the window, down into the dark ravine beyond, filled with brush and thorn bushes. Her nightgown began to smoke, the lace trim melting and burning into her skin. She was terrified of heights anyway, but now facing the idea of jumping as everything around her burned was too much.

"I can't do it, Dewey!" she screamed.

Orville moved back toward the window and pulled the overalls on. The arthritis in his hands, elbows and knees made each movement painful causing him to struggle to put each leg through. Carefully fastening the side buttons, he pulled the bib and straps up and began to move to the window, coughing and gagging from the blinding smoke. He couldn't see that the overalls were starting to smoke.

"Dad! Where are you? What are you doing? Dad, you have to jump!" Neil pleaded as he looked up at the empty window.

"Honey, where are you? Orville, please come back! Orville, honey, you've got to jump! We can't come up and get you!" The yelling caused Sarah to choke, her lungs still filled with smoke, and she doubled over, trying to clear her lungs.

Neil continued to scream and plead with Orville to come back to the window.

Within a few seconds, Orville appeared and looked down, still coughing. He grabbed the burning window frame and saw Neil standing there below, begging him to jump. The flames flew out the window around him, burning his hair and scalp as he stood, preparing himself. He heard a loud crash behind him and the sound of screaming, then looked to his left to see the burning bed drop as the floor below it began to collapse. His overalls burst into flames.

He looked at Neil, made eye contact, and jumped.

Orville outweighed Neil by 100 pounds, so when he landed, Sarah tried to grab some piece of him to help break the fall. The force of attempting to catch Orville knocked Neil to the ground. Sarah crawled over and beat out the flames on Orville's overalls as he rolled off of Neil, shaken up from the jump. His head and arms badly burned and coughing hard, Orville couldn't speak. His lungs hurt and the coughing gagged him to the point of retching.

"Honey, we are burning alive! You have to jump!" Dewey screamed as Virginia stood frozen, terrified as everything and everyone burned around her.

Virginia turned again to the window. As she got positioned,

Dewey put his hand in the middle of her back and gave her a hard shove.

"Oh God, Dewey, no!"

Screaming, Virginia flew out the window, falling too far forward from Dewey's push, and missed the grassy area by the house. She crashed through the sycamore tree, then into the ravine. Her left arm dislocated when she hit a large branch during the fall, and she cracked several ribs hitting branches on the way down, bouncing off of one onto another. She slammed onto the ground below, landing on a large tree root running along the surface, the impact breaking her pelvis as she bounced, barely conscious, into a thicket of briars.

From the bedroom window, Dewey watched her fall, and saw that his shove pushed her out too far, as she hit the branches of the tree then disappeared into the darkness of the ravine below. Fearing she was severely injured, he knew that she couldn't help him as he jumped with Gary.

"Dammit."

He looked at Gary. Huge tears ran down the toddler's blackened face, his eyes wide with terror as he looked at Dewey and screamed.

"Owie, Daddy! Owie!" he screamed as he clung tightly to his father's neck.

"It's going to be okay, buddy," Dewey said as he kissed his son on the cheek.

Lifting his right foot to step into the window frame, the floorboard beneath his left foot collapsed, weakened by the flames below.

Oh shit!

After hitting his head on the ground when his father landed on him and knocked him down, Neil regained his senses, reaching behind his head to feel for a bump. He shook his head and got to his feet while Orville collapse to the ground, exhausted from coughing, his clothes smoking.

"Mom and Dad, you need to get away from the house," Neil pleaded, leaning over to them. Kneeling down, without thinking he laid his hands on his parents' burned and blackened shoulders. Orville flinched and Sarah cried out as he touched them, hitting blister upon blister, where burned skin hung off them. Neil quickly recoiled.

Then the three of them heard it at the same time: a scream coming from within the burning home.

"Neil! Neil! Help me, I'm burning alive!"

It was Dewey.

Reeling backward as he fell through the floor, Dewey instinctively wrapped his arms tightly around Gary, who was still screaming. Together they fell through the inferno that was once the kitchen.

Can't let go! Can't let go! Oh God!

Below the kitchen was a small fruit cellar, which all six of Orville's sons helped dig by hand during the renovation in 1955. Hitting the burning kitchen floor, Dewey and Gary smashed through the weakened beams. The middle of Dewey's back hit a large stone foundation support, forcing his arms violently outward. He lost his grip on Gary, who screamed as he flew out of Dewey's arms and hit another stone support five feet away, killing him instantly.

Turning to reach his now-lifeless son, Dewey writhed in the burning pile of embers, trying to get up as the flames consumed him and burning pieces of the second floor fell on and around him. His back and legs, broken when he slammed violently into the cellar, were useless.

Oh God! Why can't I move? Where's Gary? Jesus, help me! I... I... Oh God, I'm dying! Oh God! Oh... Oh... Neil!

"Neil! Neil! Help me, I'm burning alive!"

Hearing Dewey scream, Sarah yelled, "Oh no! Oh no! Dewey!"

Sarah jumped up as Neil ran around to the front of the house, while Orville remained doubled over on the ground, coughing hard, his overalls still smoking. Screaming "Dewey!" at the top of her lungs, Sarah ran to the back of the house, to the flaming remains of the door which would have been everyone's exit if the stairs hadn't been burning.

"Neil!" Dewey screamed from somewhere within the flames.

"Dewey!" both Neil and Sarah yelled back simultaneously.

At the front of the house, Neil ran up the steps onto the porch, the overhang fully engulfed in flames. Sarah stepped closer to the rear of the house, trying to see her son through the inferno.

"Neil, help me!"

"Dewey, where are you?" Neil pleaded, running toward the kitchen door.

"Dewey! Dewey, where are you?" Sarah cried out as she stood at the back of the house, the flames licking at her eagerly.

"Mom! Neil! Help me!"

Ignoring the heat burning her flesh, Sarah stepped closer to the burning home, looking down into the cellar area. She saw a black, almost skeletal arm reach up through the burning rubble. Then she saw Dewey's blackened head turning back toward the sound of her screams.

"Oh my God! Dewey! Neil, I see him! I see him! Dewey!"

Sarah took a step forward into the burning structure and reached out to get to Dewey.

"Mom, look out!" Neil screamed just as part of the second-floor bedroom came crashing down, covering Dewey with more flaming lumber. Burning embers flew in all directions from the impact, some imbedding themselves in the remains of Sarah's nightgown, setting it on fire and burning into her. New blisters boiled up on Sarah's flesh as she recoiled from the flames.

"My God, Neil, I saw him!" she screamed as she backed away, finally noticing the cinders that burned through her nightgown, now imbedding into her skin. "Oh my God! Oh my God! I'm on fire! I'm on fire, Neil! Dewey! Neil, get Dewey!"

Neil looked inside the kitchen, hoping to see Dewey. He caught sight of a mass of burning material moving, with Dewey underneath trying to get out.

"Neil! Pleeeeease! I'm burning!"

"Dewey!" Neil screamed.

Still hearing his mother screaming from the other side of the house, Neil leapt into the burning kitchen, his body searing in the inferno that enveloped him. All around him was nothing but fire. The flames licked at his body, stinging his eyes. He heard creaking and a deep, low moaning. Shielding his eyes, he backed toward the door as the flaming remains of the second floor gave way and fell, along with the melting bedframe and burning dresser. His eyes still closed from the stinging; he didn't see a flaming beam swing forward. It struck Neil in the forehead, knocking him backwards out of the kitchen and onto the porch.

"Neil, my God, I'm dying!"

"Neil! Neil! Oh God! Neil, get Dewey!"

Shaking off the impact and hearing the continued screams from his dying brother and injured mother, Neil got up and looked again in the kitchen doorway, which was now blocked by the beam. He tried to figure out a way to squeeze in past the burning beam but there was no way in.

My God, I have to save him. I have to!

Ignoring the pain of his burns and the blood running down his face from the gash in his forehead, he turned, jumped off the porch and ran around to the south side of the house, looking for a way in, but had to back away as the flames reached for him.

"Dewey, where are you?"

"Neil!"

Running around to the back of the house, he saw his mother trying to pat out the flames on her nightgown, continuing to scream from the pain of the burns.

Then, in an instant, he noticed the deafening silence.

There was no more screaming.

He and Sarah looked at each other, their eyes wide with terror.

"Oh God, Neil! He… he's gone! Neil, he's gone! Oh God, no!" Sarah brought her burned, blistered hands up to her face and began to sob.

Neil fell to his knees, buried his scorched face in his burned hands, and wailed.

"Oh God, Dewey! Oh my God! I tried to save you! I couldn't! I just couldn't!"

He turned to his mom.

"I promise I tried, Mom! I did all I could! Oh God, Mom, I tried!"

Sarah doubled over and screamed, holding her abdomen. No words came out, just a long, pained wail. She took in a deep breath and fell forward onto the ground and let out another long, uncontrollable scream.

Neil, still doubled over a few feet away, wailed uncontrollably into his burned hands.

After screaming until she was exhausted, Sarah rolled over on the ground, still being seared from the heat of the burning house.

Drawing in her breath and wiping her eyes, a new wave of terror swept over Sarah.

"Neil… Neil…" She could barely catch her breath. "Neil… honey… did you see Virginia? Where's my Gary?" she began to panic, looking around wildly.

Neil, still sobbing, sat up and looked around, "Oh God. I didn't see Virginia anywhere. And I never saw Gary, either."

Suddenly they heard a loud cough and realized they had left Orville on the north side of the house, doubled over and coughing from all the smoke he had inhaled.

"Oh my God, Orville!"

Tears streaming down her blackened face, Sarah got up and hobbled around to the north side of the house, with Neil following closely behind her. They saw Orville, still doubled over on all fours and trying to crawl further away from the house. Together, they leaned over and helped Orville to his feet, half stumbling to the big oak tree in the front yard. Orville could barely walk, coughing and retching the whole way.

Once they reached the tree, Sarah let go of Orville and collapsed on the cold wet ground and began to shiver and cry. Neil helped Orville to the ground, leaning him against the tree.

"Neil, honey, we have to find Virginia and Gary," Sarah panted, barely able to speak in her exhaustion.

"Momma, I don't think we can look for them on our own. We gotta get help. I'm gonna run to the Pledger's place up the road and get them to help us."

Without waiting for an answer, he took off running in the cold, windy darkness, barefoot and clad only in his underwear.

4

2:37 a.m.
Hunter Road, near the farmhouse, Ava, Missouri

Ignore the cold. Ignore the cold. God, I hope George is home. I hope I can wake him up. Damn it's cold. Damn that rock hurt. Dewey! Oh God, Dewey! I should have done more. This is all my fault. God, I hope George is home. I hope he doesn't meet me at the door with his shotgun. Ignore the cold. This is all my fault.

Shivering in the near-freezing windy night, Neil ran the half mile uphill to the nearest house, the home of George and Carrie Pledger, his mind spinning all the way.

Run faster, Neil. Run faster. This is all my fault. I should have done more to save Dewey. Must run faster. Dewey! Dewey! Virginia! Gary! Driveway coming up. Must run faster. These rocks sure hurt.

Rounding the corner into the front yard, Neil picked up speed, racing to the front door of the darkened farmhouse.

Please be home. Please be home. Please wake up for me.

He pounded hard on the door repeatedly.

"Mr. Pledger! Mr. Pledger! Mr. Pledger, please wake up! Mr. Pledger, it's Neil Ritter! I gotta use your phone! Mr. Pledger, please wake up! The house! Fire! The house is on fire! Mr. Pledger! We need to call! Fire! Mr. Pledger! We need help!"

He pounded again on the door.

"Mr. Pledger! Please wake up! It's Neil Ritter! Mr. Pledger, the fire! Mr. Pledger, please we need help!"

Suddenly the lights in the living room came on while Neil continued to pound on the door and yell. The front porch light came on and George Pledger opened the door, his eyes popping open as he looked upon the blackened figure in front of him.

"Get in here, boy, you're gonna freeze to death."

Neil stumbled in, panting and crying.

"Mr. Pledger… I'm so sorry… to wake you up… our house… on fire… Mom and Dad... are out… burned bad… Virginia… is missing… Dewey… he's gone… Oh God, he's gone… can't find the baby… the floor… he… he fell through… I couldn't… couldn't… get to him… he screamed… he called my name… I heard him die…"

Carrie Pledger, George's wife of 42 years, stepped into the room, adjusting her pink flannel robe. She stopped and gasped when she saw Neil, black from head to toe, burned, shivering, and crying as George tried to comfort him.

"Carrie, honey, get the boy some clothes," George said, "Neil, sit down and try to warm up. I'm going to call Paul Pitts to get the sheriff and fire department."

Paul Pitts, who lived further west on Hunter Road, not only had the local farm phone system at his house, he also had a separate phone line that connected to the main system running to Ava. Only Pitts could call quickly to get help.

Neil sat down carefully on the couch.

"People are hurt, Mr. Pledger. And Dewey is dead. We need an ambulance." Tears rolled down Neil's blackened face.

"I'll have him call for ambulances, too." George nodded then left the room.

A few moments later, Carrie brought in a pair of George's pants and a shirt, plus one of his old jackets.

"Here, dear. These are a little too big for you, but the pants have suspenders so they'll stay up. Can I get you a drink of water?"

"Yes, ma'am," Neil choked out, trying to catch his breath. "That… would be… nice..."

"Make it quick, Carrie," George bellowed, walking back into the room, "I called Pitts. We gotta get over to that house."

George helped Neil gently pull on the oversized clothes just as Carrie brought in a glass of water. After a couple of quick gulps, he choked out a quick "thank you" then ran out to the Pledger's station wagon with George and headed back to the burning farmhouse.

"Damn, it's cold tonight," George muttered.

"I can see my breath," Neil hoarsely whispered, slowly settling into his seat.

George fired up the car and backed quickly out of the driveway, slamming the transmission into first gear and floored the gas pedal to race to whatever remained of the Ritter place.

Pulling into the driveway and crossing the bridge over the gully, the headlights from George's car caught the blackened figures of Sarah and Orville on the ground by the oak tree in the front yard. Both were on their hands and knees. Orville was coughing and retching from the smoke, Sarah beside him, trying to comfort him as he struggled with every breath. Behind them, the remains of the house continued to burn. Part of the north wall still stood, burning, and the wood stove laid on its side, glowing red from the heat. In the area that was once the kitchen, the gas cook stove laid overturned while the refrigerator eerily stood, blackened, flames continuing to dance around it.

"Oh my God," whispered George, pulling up into the grass behind the remains of the house. "I'd better pull up here, boy, to give the fire truck some room when it gets here."

Neil nodded then they both got out and ran over to where Sarah and Orville shivered against the tree. Orville struggled to get up, but George stopped him.

"Orv, don't get up," George bellowed, "Paul Pitts has called the sheriff and fire department, and we've got Clinkingbeard's ambulances on the way. Everything is going to be okay. I'm so sorry about your home."

Orville caught his breath and turned his head.

"Thanks… George" was all he could get out.

George leaned over to get a closer look at Sarah and Orville. Thinking he was going to rest his hand on Orville's shoulder, he pulled back, horrified by the burns he saw on his friend's back, arms, and hands.

Jesus, the skin is just hanging off of him. Any place that isn't black has burned skin hanging off and blood. Dear God, the blood.

He took a quick look at Sarah and saw much the same. Her nightgown hung onto her body in singed pieces, and in some places the burned skin intermingled with the blood and bits of nightgown.

As long as I live, I don't ever want to see anything like this again.

"Where's Virginia, Orv? Isn't she here too? I thought I heard she was here."

Orville couldn't stop coughing long enough to answer.

"We haven't seen her. We're... we're not sure. If she got out... she may be down in that gulley. Hopefully she has Gary," Neil spoke up from behind George.

"I've got a flashlight. Let me see if I can find her for you." George ran to his car and pulled the large metal flashlight from under his seat.

"God, I hope the batteries are good."

George turned it on and shook it hard. The flashlight lit up brightly. Breathing a sigh of relief, George ran behind the house and looked for a moment into the remains of the house in the kitchen area. Had he looked more closely, he would have noticed a black outstretched skeletal arm sticking out of a pile of burning embers near the center of where the floor had been. George stopped at the edge of the gulley and shown the flashlight down into the blackness below. Peering through the brush and trying to scan the area, he had to be careful where he stepped. The overwhelming heat from the burning house singed his skin, so he stayed as far away as possible. Giving up on that position, George ran around the house and to another clearing in hopes of seeing better down into the gulley, silently praying to find Virginia there amongst the bushes and scrub trees.

Just as he began to scan the area with his flashlight, to the right of where he was looking he heard the faint sound of a woman calling for help. He quickly shifted to the right, and the light caught the form of the broken and bleeding Virginia, lying at the bottom of the gulley.

"Thank God she's alive," he muttered to himself.

"Virginia! Don't move, dear! Help is coming! We are going to get you out of there! Just hang on, dear!"

George ran back over to the Orville, Sarah, and Neil, still shivering against the tree.

"I found Virginia," George announced. "She appears to be hurt bad but she's alive. She's down in the bottom of the gulley, and we're going to need help to get her out."

Neil started to get up, but George waved him off.

"No, boy, you're cold and hurt enough as it is. The Pitts should be here any minute, and the fire department and sheriff. They will help us. You three just stay put now, ya hear?"

Neil and Sarah nodded just as headlights hit the driveway announcing the arrival of the Pitts.

"I'm here to help," shouted a voice from the driveway.

"Carrie, is that you?" George Pledger recognized his wife's voice in the dark.

"Yes, dear, I walked down here, I want to help. Did I hear you say you found Virginia? Did I hear that right?" Carrie pulled the collar up on the coat she had thrown over her nightgown as the Pitts car brushed past her.

"I found her in the ditch, Carrie," George said, pointing toward the area where he saw her.

"Is anyone down there with her?"

"No, dear, we're gonna have to figure out how to get her out of there."

"Poor thing, she's down there by herself. Show me where she is. I'm going to go down there and stay with her till you get something figured out." Carrie adjusted her coat and checked to make sure all her buttons were snug.

"Woman, you can't go down there! It's full of brush and…"

"George Pledger!" Carrie interrupted, "I grew up on the farm down the road from yours. If I can throw my brothers out of a blackberry patch, I can sure crawl down into that spot to comfort that girl. Now show me where she is! Let's quit talkin' and start doin'!"

George quit protesting and took his wife by the hand and walked her down the driveway to the gate that led to the garden area. Opening the gate, he shone the flashlight over to the big sycamore tree.

"You see that tree, dear?" George nodded toward the tree.

"Yes, George. Is she by that tree?"

"She's about ten feet this side of it. She looks bad. Take this flashlight to make your way through the brush. And be careful, woman!" George bellowed.

Taking the flashlight, Carrie passed through the gate and began pushing her way through the brush, keeping an eye on the sycamore tree.

"Virginia, honey, where are you?" Carrie called out.

"I'm here. Please help me," came the weak response from darkness. The fire illuminated the upper branches of the tree, but the lower half was plunged in complete darkness. Following the sound, Carrie pushed her way through the scrubby bushes and briars, cutting her arms, till the flashlight suddenly illuminated the broken and bleeding Virginia.

Carrie looked up to where the house previously stood.

Dear God. She fell from the second story window?

She looked back down at Virginia.

I've got to keep her calm. Those guys better do whatever to get her out of this ditch, but I've got to keep her calm.

Carrie laid down beside Virginia, pressing her face against the injured young lady.

Thank God she's alive.

"Virginia, honey, it's Carrie Pledger. I live just up the road. Honey, I'm going to stay with you till the men up there figure out how to get you out of this area." Carrie took a hankie out of her coat and wiped Virginia's forehead and cheeks.

"Oh, Mrs. Pledger. Thank you," Virginia whispered, beginning to cry. "I… I didn't think anyone… was going to… find me."

"My George found you." Carrie smiled. "I'm not leaving till we get you out of here."

"Dewey… my Dewey… Dewey's gone, Mrs. Pledger. And… my little boy… my little boy is gone, too. I heard… I heard Gary crying. I heard Dewey… Dewey was screaming. Oh, Mrs. Pledger. I… I should have… jumped… jumped sooner. I was so scared. I didn't… want my baby to get hurt."

"It's okay, dear. Just rest. Help is coming," Carrie whispered.

Carrie looked up, hearing the sound of distant sirens cutting the stillness. Through the brush, she caught a glimpse of the Pitts' headlights.

Paul Pitts stopped the car in the front yard as his wife Modena jumped out with arms full of sheets. She stepped quickly to the huddled figures by the tree, illuminated by the glow of the burning home. Modena knelt down toward Sarah with open arms, then recoiled, dropping the sheets.

"Honey, I don't want to hurt your burns," Modena cried, "Oh Sarah, you're hurt so bad. I'm so sorry."

"Thank you" was all Sarah could get out, collapsing into her friend's arms, sobbing into her shoulder.

The icy wind began blowing again. George pulled his coat around his neck then picked up the pile of sheets beside the two ladies, walking them over to Orville and Neil. Paul parked his car beside George's near the hay barn. Carrying a thermos, he ran to the tree where George stood near the family. At his feet, Neil was sitting and crying loudly. Nearby Orville remained on all fours, coughing.

"We brought sheets instead of blankets. We figured blankets would be too heavy on their burns. Here, this is water," Paul said, holding up the thermos.

George took the water thermos from Paul's hand and walked it over to Orville and knelt down.

"Here, neighbor, you need to drink."

George kept Orville steady as he drank from the thermos. After swallowing a couple of swigs, he handed the thermos back to George.

"Better, Orv?"

Orville could only nod then collapsed on the ground.

George looked up at Paul, both men fighting back tears.

"I think we need to try to protect them from this wind, George," Paul choked out. "Let's hold these sheets up and see if it helps. Modena, dear, please help us."

Modena got up and helped Paul and George unfold sheets. Together they stood in a semicircle. George and Paul stood facing south, with George curving slightly toward the family on the left side. They stood two arms' lengths apart, with Modena at a right angle to Paul with her back facing west. Together they held up the sheets and stood on whatever amount of cloth was piled up at their feet. Pulling the sheets up tight and stretching their arms wide, the three held the sheets around Neil, Orville, and Sarah to protect them from the cold blasts of wind that blew in from the north.

George looked to his left, as the remains of the house continued to burn, flames dancing up toward the sky. He listened to the ever-present sound of the crackling of the wood burning and the occasional sound of pieces of wall falling in.

Dewey is in there. My God, he is just lying in there burning. We can't even get to him.

He looked back at the three burned bodies of his neighbors on the ground at his feet, choking back tears, as the sirens drew near.

Thank God. Here comes the cavalry.

5

George, Paul, and Modena continued to hold sheets up around the Ritters as the Douglas County Sherriff arrived, followed closely by the Ava Fire Department truck. Sheriff Don Souder parked in the front yard between the burning remains of the house and the group by the tree. Just as he stepped out of his cruiser, the remains of the north wall fell in, spraying glowing embers into the moonlit night. He stood and looked at the burning mass, then turned and walked quickly toward the group.

"Orville, Sarah, Neil," he said, nodding to each, "I'm sure sorry to hear about all this. Is everyone okay?"

"No, Don, we've got a bad situation here," George Pledger spoke up. "Orville, Sarah, and Neil are burned bad. Virginia is injured, I fear she's severely hurt. I found her lying down there at the bottom of that gully, down in Orv's old garden. Carrie is down there with her right now," George said, turning and pointing.

"And she's pregnant, Don! Virginia is pregnant!" sobbed Sarah, curled up in the cold grass.

"What about Dewey and his little boy?" Sheriff Souder asked, "I haven't seen him since he got home."

George was silent, his eyes tearing up.

"We are not sure where little Gary is. We're hoping Virginia has him, but I didn't see him with her. And Dewey is somewhere in there, Sheriff," George said, turning and nodding toward the house.

Sarah began to sob again as Modena leaned down and carefully laid her hand on her friend, not wanting to inflict more pain in Sarah's burned flesh.

"I tried to help him! I tried to get to him! It's all my fault! I couldn't get to him!" Neil cried, burying his face in the grass, breathing so hard, he nearly hyperventilated.

Don turned white and took off his hat.

"Oh no. Oh no, no, no! No, that can't be! They just got home!"

George put his hand on the sheriff's shoulder.

The fire truck pulled in close to the house, and its four occupants clambered out quickly to start applying water to the remains of the house.

"I'd better get Clarence Clinkingbeard here, George," Don said, pulling away from the group.

"I called for the ambulances. But I didn't think to ask for Clarence," Paul called out as the trio continued to hold sheets over the family.

With a heavy sigh, Don walked around to the driver's side of his cruiser, opened the door, and sat down inside to radio the office. He sat for a moment and collected his thoughts before hitting the button. Clarence Clinkingbeard, who owned the funeral home and ambulance service that bore his family name, was also the Douglas County Coroner, so he needed to be on the scene.

God, this is awful.

"Sheriff Souder to base. Come in base."

"Base."

"Linda, I need you to get hold of Clinkingbeard. I'm out here at Orville Ritter's place on Hunter Road. We have at least one casualty in this fire so he needs to be here."

"Roger that. Will do, Sheriff. Tell Sarah that Robert and I will keep her family in our prayers."

"Will do, Linda. Thank you."

Sheriff Souder wiped his forehead with his sleeve then stepped back out, staring at the wreckage of the home.

"Damn," he whispered, walking back over to the group assembled by the tree.

"I've got Linda dispatching Clinkingbeard. You know, his ambulances may only be able to take two or three folks. I'm going to need at least one more vehicle to get everyone transported."

“Neil… Neil and me… we… we’ll be ok,” Orville coughed.

“No, Orv, that won’t do.” Sheriff Souder leaned down over his friend. “You’ve been badly burned, and it sounds like you swallowed a bunch of smoke. And Neil’s burned, too. All four of you need to go to Springfield to be treated.”

“St. John’s?” George inquired. St. John’s Hospital in Springfield was over an hour away but was the closest facility with the capability to treat burn victims.

“I think that’s their best bet,” the sheriff answered, turning to George.

“Don, I can take one of them,” George said, “I’ll be your third vehicle.”

“Okay, thanks, George.” Sheriff Souder shook hands with him. “Right now we need to figure out how to get Virginia out of that ditch before the ambulances get here.”

“You’re gonna need a flashlight. Carrie’s got mine with her,” George noted.

“Thanks, George.” Sheriff Souder nodded, walking over to his car to dig out the flashlight from the glove box. He then turned to the nearest fireman, who was watching the gauges on the truck.

“Hey, Steven! Do you guys have a rescue cage on that thing?”

“Afraid not, Sheriff! But we do have a stretcher over here. Will that help?”

“You bet,” the sheriff called out, running toward the truck. The fireman pulled the stretcher out of the lower compartment on the truck and handed it to him.

“Thanks, Steven. Hey, Paul and George!” Sheriff Souder shouted as he walked down the driveway toward the gate that led to the truck patch. “You guys keep protecting them, and I’m going to see if me and Carrie can get Virginia out of that gulley!”

“Let me help,” Steven hollered as he motioned for one of the other firemen to come over and watch the gauges.

Another neighbor, Leonard Burk, pulled up in his box truck as Steven and Sheriff Souder walked quickly down the driveway. Leonard walked over to Modena, Paul, and George, who were still holding up sheets to shield the family from the wind.

"Do you have another sheet?" Leonard asked. "I can join in helpin' this situation."

"There you go, neighbor, right there on the ground." Paul smiled, nodding toward his left.

Leonard looked at how everyone was holding their sheets as he unfolded his. Standing on it like the others, he held it up next to Modena.

"Paul, we need to pray out loud or something," Modena blurted out, turning to her husband, "This is horrible! Our neighbors are hurting and we need to do something to lift their spirits."

Paul turned and looked at Modena. In the light of the flames and red fire truck lights, he saw his beloved wife, tears streaming down her face, completely overwhelmed by the horror unfolding before her.

His eyes softened, and he smiled at her, then closed his eyes and began to sing loudly:

"What a friend we have in Jesus…"

Modena joined in.

"All our sins and grieves to bear…"

Then George and Leonard joined in loudly.

"What a privilege to carry
Everything to God in prayer…"

Down in the gulley below the burning remains of the house, Carrie huddled over Virginia in the cold darkness of the night, waiting for help to get her out of there. Carrie gently brushed Virginia's hair back with her fingers as they both fought back tears. When the Pitts, George Pledger and Leonard Burk started singing, they both looked toward the top of the hill.

"Do you hear that, dear?" Carrie asked quietly.

"Yes ma'am. I love that song. We… we used to sing it… at the church services on the… on the Air Force base in France," Virginia squeaked out, her voice raspy.

Carrie sang quietly to her, with the rest of them,

"Have we trials and temptations,
Is there trouble anywhere
If we don't be discouraged…"

Virginia weakly chimed in on the last line,

"Take it to the Lord in prayer."

"Atta girl. Honey, are you in a lot of pain?" Carrie inquired softly, the singing continuing overhead.

"Yes ma'am."

"Can you tell me where it hurts?"

"Well," Virginia struggled with the words, "I'm… I'm pretty sure… my left arm… is broken. I can't… can't… move it at all."

"Okay, dear. What else hurts?"

"My hip… it hurts bad… I landed… hard… it sounded… sounded like… a huge crack… when I hit." Virginia struggled with each word.

"Okay," Carrie whispered. "Does anything else hurt?"

"My ankle… my left ankle… hurts really really bad."

"Anything else, love?"

"No ma'am, I don't think so."

"Okay, dear. When the guys get down here to help you get out, I will let them know where it hurts. We want to be very careful with you." Carrie looked down at Virginia's right arm. She could see the arm was badly burned but saw no other outward signs of injury.

"Mrs. Pledger?"

"Call me Carrie, dear."

Virginia tried to smile despite the pain.

"Carrie… I wasn't… I wasn't sure… if anyone… was gonna find me... I tried… I tried to call out… call out for help… but I can't… I can't yell very loud... It hurts."

She stopped for a moment, tears welling up in her eyes.

"Please tell them… tell them to be careful… I'm with child. I mean… my baby… I'm…" Unable to maintain her composure, Virginia began to sob uncontrollably. "I think I… I think I killed my baby… when I hit... hit the ground."

Carrie leaned in against Virginia's face and held her gently. The two women cried quietly together.

Don and Steven walked down the driveway to the gate that led to the old garden. With the help of Don's flashlight, they found Carrie's trampled path through the weeds and brush to get to

Virginia, then shone the light on the two women, huddled closely together.

The sheriff knelt down over the scared, injured Virginia.

"Don't you worry, Miss Virginia. It's all going to be okay now. We've got you," Sheriff Souder whispered, leaning down close to her face.

"Dewey told me… he told me… he was burning… he wanted me… to jump... I… I didn't… I couldn't… I didn't jump… soon enough, Sheriff… It's all my fault," she whispered and started crying again.

"Shhhh, now, Virginia, honey, it's not your fault," the sheriff consoled her. "You quit going on like that now, ya hear? It's not your fault."

Sheriff Souder paused for a moment.

"Miss Virginia, I'm afraid to ask this… Did you jump with Gary? Is he down here?"

Virginia began to sob.

"No Sheriff… He… Dewey… Dewey was holding him… when he pushed me out the window… Dewey… Dewey was holding him… when he fell…" She began to cry harder. "They fell together Sheriff."

Virginia turned to Carrie and sobbed uncontrollably. Carrie leaned down over her and cried with her.

Sheriff Souder took off his hat, lowered his head, and muttered, "Jesus."

After a slight pause, the sheriff raised his head again, his eyes red with tears.

"Virginia, I'm so sorry. No one up there realizes little Gary fell with him. I'm so sorry."

He looked up the hill where the house had been then looked back at Virginia. "Honey, you're hurt very badly. Let's get you out of this mess, okay?"

Virginia mouthed "okay" while continuing to cry. Sheriff Souder reached out his arm to help Carrie up.

"Let's get you out of here ahead of this, Mrs. Pledger." Sheriff Souder stood back up.

"No, Don, I'd really like to stay and at least walk along beside her. You guys need to watch her arms, hips, and left ankle. She says those places on her hurt bad, may be broken. Please be careful."

Carrie grabbed the sheriff's arm and pulled him in close.

"She's hurt bad, Don. This is awful. It just breaks my heart."

"We'll be careful." Don winked.

Carrie let go of Don's arm and walked back over to Virginia's side and held her hand.

"Okay, let's make a plan to get her out of here," the sheriff said, looking around. "I think we should be able to walk her out of here, but there's a lot of brush between here and that gate."

"It seemed like the brush got a little thinner to the south over there," Steven said, pointing. "I couldn't see it real clear, but I think it looks a little easier over there."

All three of them looked over toward the driveway and the bridge that spanned the gulley. Sheriff Souder took off his hat and rubbed his head.

"There's sure a lot of brush between here and there. I'll walk over there, Steven, and see if it thins out like you say."

Don pushed his way through the brush, stomping down as much as he could along the way while shining the flashlight toward the creek to the south.

"Yep, Steven, you were right," Sheriff Souder called out. "It thins out a little over here. We're gonna have to be careful, but we can get her out this way."

He ran back over and handed Carrie his flashlight.

"Steven, let's get that stretcher unrolled," he said, then leaned over Virginia. "Miss Virginia, we're gonna have to get you on this stretcher so that we can get you out of here, okay? We're gonna be real careful, but, honey, I need you to be brave. This may hurt but we've got to do this to get you out of here."

"Okay Sheriff… Thank you… I'll… be brave."

Don took in a deep breath.

"Alright, let's do this."

With Carrie beside Virginia, the sheriff at her head and Steven at her feet, the three gently rolled her on her side to get the stretcher under her. She shrieked in pain and bit down on her lower lip, sobbing. Carrie gasped, tears at once streaming down her face.

"Oh, please be careful!" Carrie pleaded.

Once the stretcher was under her, they returned her to lying flat on her back.

"I know that hurt, Virginia, but you're on the stretcher now.

We've got a little bit of walking to get you out of here, but we're getting there, okay?"

"Okay," she squeaked, still crying from the pain.

"Alright, let's go. She needs to go up feet first so I'll lead. Watch your step but let's move quickly. Lift on the count of three. One. Two. Three!"

The sound of the Clinkingbeard ambulances could be heard in the distance, as the men worked their way through the brush with their precious cargo. Sheriff Souder walked backwards, looking over his shoulder. After nearly tripping a couple of times, Carrie hollered for them to stop.

"Let me get ahead of you, Don," suggested Carrie, "I've got the flashlight, let me blaze the trail for you boys."

Not waiting for approval, she slid past the sheriff and took the lead.

"I'll warn you if I see anything treacherous, Sheriff."

"Thank you, Carrie. I don't want to fall with her." Don's breath was visible in the cold as he continued walking backward through the brush.

All three were panting and grunting as they worked feverishly, fumbling in the dark, trying to get footing to bring Virginia up out of the gulley. Virginia lay on the stretcher, quiet as a mouse, as the two men worked hard.

Suddenly Don lost his footing and his left foot slid out from under him.

"Oh no!" he cried as his right leg buckled and he hit the ground hard. "Carrie, help!"

Sheriff Souder's end of the stretcher went down as he slipped and fell, but he managed to keep from dumping Virginia out of it. He was almost completely underneath the stretcher when he finally steadied himself. Seeing him fall, Carrie ran over and grabbed the stretcher.

"I've got her, Don. Come on out of there," Carrie strained.

Don rolled out from under the stretcher and struggled to his feet.

"Wow. Take a moment to breathe. Set her down," Sheriff Souder panted, leaning over to catch his breath.

"I'm… so sorry…" Virginia sobbed as she and the stretcher settled back down onto the ground.

"Now, now," the sheriff comforted her, catching his breath.

"Honey… you don't owe… any apologies. You don't weigh anything… my foot… just slipped out from under me. Don't you… don't you worry about it none."

Sheriff Souder took a deep breath and walked back to the foot of the stretcher while Carrie stepped back, still handling the flashlight.

"Sorry, Don." Carrie shook her head. "I never saw anything on the ground. I don't know what you slipped on."

"Don't worry about it, Carrie," Don reassured her. "My foot just slipped. This ground's a little wet. I'm just glad we didn't dump her. That would have been bad."

"Are we ready?" Steven asked the group.

"Let's do it." Don breathed in deep, strengthening his grip on the stretcher.

"On three… One, two, three!" Don and Steven grunted as they lifted Virginia's stretcher up again and started working their way to the gate at the driveway with Carrie leading the way, shining the flashlight on the path. Everyone looked up when the headlights of the two ambulances crested the hill with red lights glowing and sirens wailing.

"Boys, I think you can see your way now, can't you?" Carrie asked.

"Yes, ma'am. What are you thinking about?" Don inquired, turning around to try to see her.

"I'm going to go over to the road to flag those ambulances in," Carrie answered, not waiting for a response, and headed down the driveway toward the road.

The thick smoke from the fire hung low in the valley as the temperature continued to drop to near freezing. Up to that point, the only light around the family had been from the flames of the collapsed remnants of the house and the red light atop the small fire truck. Now, the smoke spread out the light from the bright headlights and revolving red beacons from the two ambulances, and the whole scene took on a haunting, surreal appearance. The smell of smoke and burning wood permeated every fiber of clothing, and all around them was wet and cold, except for the flames.

Carrie stood in the middle of the rocky road to wave the

ambulances into the driveway, while Steven and Sheriff Souder walked quickly up the driveway with Virginia. They ran her over to the oak tree where the rest of the family was huddled and laid her down in the grassy yard. Sarah got up and ran over to her. Though every movement hurt, she got down on her knees and kissed Virginia's cheek as both women began to cry again.

"Oh, mama… I'm so sorry… It's my fault... I should have… I should have… jumped sooner... He said... he was burning… I was… I was scared, Mama... I was so scared... I didn't… I didn't want… to hurt… the baby. I… I should have… jumped sooner… Oh, Mama… I'm so sorry."

"Shhhhh, honey. That's enough of that talk. Rest, dear, try not to talk," Sarah whispered as she held Virginia's face against hers. "Honey, it's not your fault…"

"Mama," Virginia interrupted, "Gary… Gary fell with Dewey… He was holding him… when he fell…"

"Oh my God! That precious baby! Oh, honey! Oh no!" Sarah shrieked and began to sob again, leaning over Virginia. The two women held each other, crying inconsolably.

Sarah eventually began to cough and choke from crying so hard and on all fours had to pull away from Virginia for a moment. She coughed and retched, as Modena leaned down, still holding the sheet.

"Honey, let's work on getting that bad air out," Modena said. Sarah's arms and legs collapsed from under her, then turned her head and rested on the cool grass, wheezing. Standing over her, Modena got a good look at Sarah's burned and bloody body. Her face was burned, and Modena could see the various places where the embers seared into her skin. Both legs were covered with blisters and open, bleeding wounds. The burns were deep and Sarah's blackened flesh hung off her around the wounds.

When Sarah pulled away, Sheriff Souder stepped back over to Virginia on the stretcher. Kneeling down, he leaned down close to Virginia, who was still crying.

"Sheriff Souder… thank you… for… for rescuing me…You… you know my parents, right?" Virginia asked quietly.

"Yes, dear," Don spoke softly, wiping Virginia's tears.

"Would you… would you please…" Virginia continued to struggle talking through the pain, "tell them… what's happened?"

"Of course, Virginia. Don't you worry none. I'll let them know." Don paused for a moment. "Sounds like you are going to get an ambulance ride to Springfield. I'm sure they will come check on you the minute I let them know."

Just then, Orville coughed hard and gagged, still on all fours on the ground. Virginia turned her head and looked his direction.

"Is Daddy… is Daddy Orv going to be okay?" She looked at the sheriff.

"Honey, he swallowed a lot of smoke. He was apparently last to jump out the window."

"Where's… where's Neil, Sheriff?"

"Neil's laying over there on the other side of Miss Sarah."

"Can you… can you ask him… to come over here… please?"

Don nodded then got up and walked over to Neil, gently knelt next to him, placing a hand on his shoulder, trying to avoid the burns. With red, crying eyes shining brightly on his blackened face, Neil turned and looked to see who was touching him.

"Neil, I know you're upset, but Miss Virginia just asked for you."

With a quick but quiet "Thank you, sir," Neil slowly got up, wiped his eyes and walked over to Virginia. He knelt down and lay on the cold wet grass next to her and grabbed her hand as the ambulances pulled into the driveway, followed by Clarence Clinkingbeard in his black sedan. Carrie walked up the driveway after them to rejoin everyone in the yard.

"Oh, Neil…" Virginia continued to fight back tears. "My Dewey… he's… he's gone isn't he?"

Tears began to roll down Neil's face.

"My baby… my little Gary… he's gone, too…" She gulped hard. "My little Gary is gone…"

Neil eyes widened. "We all hoped Gary was with you!"

"No, Dewey was holding him when he pushed me out the window…" Virginia cried.

"Oh God! Oh no!" Neil shrieked.

"Neil," Virginia grabbed Neil's hand, "I think my baby… this little one… we don't… we don't even know if… if it's… if it's a boy or girl… I think… it's gone too, Neil… it's still… still inside me… but it's… gone, too, Neil…" She began to sob.

Neil leaned in, breathing hard, his face pressing against the side of Virginia's head.

"He was screaming. Screaming!" Neil sobbed, "I tried to get to him, Virginia. I tried. He was calling my name!"

"I know, Neil… I… I heard him… screaming… I was… laying in… laying in that ditch… crying… listening… listening to him scream."

"I'm so sorry, sis. I'm so sorry. I tried so hard to get to him. I tried, I promise I tried. I tried!" Neil leaned over against Virginia.

"I know you did," Virginia whispered, trying to smile, her hand gently cradling Neil's face. "Dewey knows you tried too."

They both began to sob loudly, then Neil started screaming uncontrollably again, repeatedly yelling "Dewey! Oh God, Dewey!"

Don stood up, leaving Neil and Virginia to grieve together, and with his hands on his hips, surveyed the scene. Orville continued to cough and retch as Sarah lay nearby on the grass, exhausted and crying. Neil and Virginia were lying side by side, her crying as he screamed. Leonard, Modena, Paul, and George stopped singing but were still standing over the family, holding the sheets to protect everyone from the wind, which continued blowing hard from the north. Modena noticed Carrie walking up the driveway. Handing her sheet to Paul and moving Leonard over to take her place, she jogged over to Carrie and wrapped her arms around her. Don watched as the ladies stood in the driveway and cried together.

No one noticed, but Sarah, still lying on the grass in her exhaustion, turned her head and looked at the burning remains of her once-proud farmhouse. All her possessions, all her pictures, all her hopes and dreams, and more importantly, her son and grandson continued to burn in the inferno, still crackling and sending burning embers into the dark cold sky.

"What a friend we have in Jesus," Sarah whispered, tears once again pouring down her blackened face. She buried her face in the cold grass, unable to look into the flames anymore.

6

Lyle Clinkingbeard and Charles Fish jumped out of their ambulances and ran over to Sheriff Souder, who was still surveying the grieving family at his feet. He turned and shook hands with both men.

"Guys, these folks are hurt badly. We need to get them to St. John's in Springfield fast. I'm wondering if we could get both Neil and Virginia in one and put Mrs. Ritter in the second one. George Pledger has already volunteered to take Mr. Ritter in his car and follow behind you guys. How does that sound?"

"Sounds good to me, Sheriff. I think for sure we can get those two in one," Lyle said, pointing at Virginia and Neil, still on the ground.

"Alright, let's make it happen then." Don clapped his hands together. "Time's a-wastin'. They need help fast."

After watching the ambulances leave with George Pledger trailing closely behind, Paul and Modena Pitts, along with Carrie Pledger and Leonard Burk, stood closely together in stunned silence, looking at the burning remains of the house. Barely blinking, the only sign of their breathing came from the vapor emanating from their open mouths in the cold night air.

"In all the excitement, I almost forgot those two souls are in there somewhere," Carrie sniffed, nodding toward the house.

"I wish there was something we could have done, some way we could have saved them," Paul uttered, barely breaking his stare.

"There's nothing you could have done, dear. Nothing anyone could have done," Modena reassured, slipping her chilled hand into Paul's.

As the four continued to stand there in the yard, sheets piled up at their feet from their efforts to protect the family, another car pulled in and parked behind the fire truck.

"I got here as soon as I heard," called out Elga Vinson, another neighbor from down the road. "Neva took the call. I can't believe this has happened."

Elga took turns hugging Carrie and Modena then sternly shook hands with Paul and Leonard.

"Orv, Sarah, Neil, and Virginia are all on their way to Springfield," Carrie sniffed. "They are burned bad, and Virginia has some broken bones from her fall."

"They had to jump from the windows, Elga. The stairs were on fire." Modena pointed to windows that were no longer there.

"Dear God. Neva said Dewey didn't make it out." Elga shook his head and looked down at the ground.

"Little Gary didn't make it out, either, Elga," Paul said blankly.

"I'm just numb. I don't know when I've cried so much." Modena brought her kerchief up to her eyes. "This is all so terrible. Poor Sarah."

As the neighbors stood looking at the burning rubble, Sheriff Souder came walking quickly toward them.

"Hey, Elga, good to see you." The sheriff extended his arm to shake hands. "I mean, you know, under the circumstances.

"Good to see you too, Don." Elga returned the handshake. "I came over as soon as I heard. I know everyone just left, but is there anything I can do to help?"

"Yes, I think so. Hang on just a second." Sheriff Souder turned toward Clarence Clinkingbeard, who was standing several feet away, near the north end of the house, hands on his hips, staring into the fire. "Hey Clarence! Can you come here?"

Clarence turned and walked toward the group. A tall, thin man, his statuesque appearance had a calming reputation with the folks of

Ava. He shook hands with each person in his normal gentle fashion, with his right hand while holding the person's arm or elbow with his left. After greeting everyone, he turned to Sheriff Souder.

"How may I be of assistance, Don?"

"Clarence, Elga here just showed up and is offering to help. Do you want to discuss with him what we talked about while the ambulances were pulling out?"

"Yes indeed." Clarence nodded, extending his hand to Elga. "Mr. Vinson, perhaps you and I could walk over here and talk for a moment. I don't want to talk about this in front of the ladies." He turned to Modena and Carrie. "Ladies, would you please excuse us?"

"Of course, Mr. Clinkingbeard." Carrie smiled weakly and nodded.

Clarence nodded at them and Paul then with Sheriff Souder tagging along, pulled Elga aside for a private conversation.

"Mr. Vinson…"

"Call me Elga, please."

"Elga, I have a delicate question to ask you, and it pertains to your offer of service in this dreadful hour," Clarence said, sternly.

"Ask away, Mr. Clinkingbeard."

"Elga," Clarence continued, "with all this rubble, I am going to have to eventually, when things cool down a bit, recover the bodies of Mr. Ritter and the child. I cannot perform this alone. Therefore, I require assistance to perform this unpleasant task. Would you be willing to assist me in this endeavor?"

Elga's face sunk and he grew pale at Clarence's request.

Jesus. Recovering the body of my neighbor and his little boy. Stand by me Jesus.

He sighed heavily.

"Yeah, Clarence, I'll help." Elga nodded. "I gotta tell ya, the idea scares the hell out of me, but I'll help."

"Thank you, Elga," Sheriff Souder spoke up, "I'd do it myself, but I need to leave right now and head to Garland Dye's house. I gotta tell them about all this. They are going to want to head to Springfield to check on Virginia."

"Indeed, I'm sure they will," Clarence agreed. "Thank you for dispatching me this morning, Sheriff."

"Thank you for getting over here so fast," Don said, shaking hands with both men. "I'll be back in a couple of hours if I can, to check on you boys."

The sheriff walked back over to Carrie, Modena, and Paul.

"He's going to help look for them, isn't he?" Modena's voice cracked.

"Yeah. I didn't want you ladies to hear that conversation." Don looked back at the smoldering remains of the house and shook his head. "Not a job I would want. I've done it before, but searching for that little boy… that's going to be tough. Look, there's nothing else you all can do," he said, turning back to them. "Thank you for everything you did. You're good neighbors, every one of you. How 'bout you all go home and try to get some rest."

"I don't know how I'll ever sleep again after this morning." Modena sniffed, leaning over to pick up the sheets at their feet.

"Miss Carrie, may we take you home since George is driving to Springfield?" Paul asked.

"Thank you, Paul, I would appreciate that," Carrie nodded as she helped collect the sheets.

7

October 27, 5:28 a.m.
St. John's Hospital, Springfield, Missouri

Mildred looked at her watch when she heard the wail of the approaching sirens.

A little over an hour since they called. Burn victims always scare me. In twenty years of nursing, I've never been able to deal with burn victims. God, give me strength.

She blinked hard and turned to walk down the ward to find Doctor Goodson, just in time to see him poke his head out from behind the curtain of an exam room. They made eye contact.

"That's probably them," he grimaced. "Is Room 11 still open?"

"Yes."

"Okay, put the pregnant lady in there." He walked toward her as he talked. "The other three are going to have to be put on gurneys and along the wall of Hall 2 over there. I don't like doing things that way, but we're just too full. I'll have to do triage on them in the hallway. Is Ferguson here yet?"

"I don't think so." Mildred shook her head, looking toward the door.

"Alright. Let me know as soon as you see him." He started to walk away, then stopped and turned back around. "Jesus, they probably haven't been on oxygen at all. First thing, I want oxygen on all four of them. Come get me when you have them in place. I'm going to see if I can get anyone out of these rooms."

Goodson walked away quickly, darting into another exam room.

Mildred ran over to the nurses' station and grabbed the intercom mic.

"I need orderlies to the ER! All available orderlies to the ER!"

The ambulance entrance to the emergency room at St. John's Hospital, little more than a wide alley between the main hospital and another medical building, sat vacant. The Clinkingbeard ambulances pulled in first and parked beside each other just past the emergency room doors, taking up the width of the alley. Before turning into the driveway, George Pledger stopped in the middle of National Avenue and sized up the alley.

I gotta back in so they can get to Orv easier.

Traffic was light at that time of morning, so he pulled forward in the road, shifted his station wagon in reverse, and backed into the alley to the emergency room doors.

"Orv, we made it to Springfield," George called back to his barely conscious passenger, who by now was breathing shallow, with an occasional cough and a definitive rattle in his lungs with every breath. "You're at St. John's my friend. Just hang in there, Orv."

Four gurneys attended by six orderlies and two nurses came swarming out of the emergency room doors. Chaos ensued as the back doors of the vehicles flew open and everyone talked at once while gently getting each victim out. Mildred ran into the alley to direct the madness.

"Where's the pregnant one?"

"Be careful how you help them out!"

"What's your name, sir?"

"I've got her over here, she's on a stretcher."

"This one here, the old guy, he isn't breathing very well. He's not telling me his name."

As the din of shouting continued, the orderlies and nurses became aware of a continuous low chorus of moans that surrounded them while they worked feverishly to get the family out of the vehicles and onto gurneys.

"What's your name, son?"

"Orville, honey, are you still with me?" Sarah called out amidst the chaos.

"Move slowly now, I've got you."

My God they look bad.

"Neil. My name is Neil."

"I just want sheets on them, no blankets!"

"What's your name, honey?"

The old guy doesn't sound good at all.

"Be careful, everyone, watch out for their blisters!"

"I've got third degree burns over here!"

"Virginia. My name is Virginia."

"The pregnant lady goes in Room 11! The rest have to line the wall in Hall 2 until Doctor Goodson can look at them! I need oxygen on all four please the moment you get them parked! Let's go people!" Mildred barked, clapping her hands together.

The doors flew open as Virginia was wheeled to Room 11. Barely conscious and in vicious pain, she gazed at the ceiling, barely aware of the people around her. Nearby, Neil, Sarah, and Orville were wheeled around the corner and parked alongside a wall to await examination by Doctor Goodson.

A young orderly stopped at Neil's gurney with an oxygen bottle.

"What's your name, sir?" the orderly asked in a soft voice.

"Neil. I'm Neil."

"Well, Neil, I'm David. I have oxygen here for you. I understand you may have inhaled some smoke. The doctor ordered that all of you need oxygen. This will just take a moment."

David gently lifted Neil's head and began to slip on the straps from an oxygen mask when he noticed Neil's burned scalp, blisters, and gash on his forehead, which by now had stopped bleeding but left a mix of blood and soot on his skin.

"Neil, I'm going to do this very carefully. I don't want this oxygen mask to hurt you, okay? You need to let me know if this is hurting you."

David carefully got the straps in place behind Neil's head while he held on to the mask.

"Okay, buddy, I'm going to lower this mask onto you. Like I said, please let me know if this hurts at all."

Moving slowly, David lowered the mask over Neil's blackened mouth and nose, then set the oxygen bottle next to the gurney.

"How is that, Neil?"

Neil turned his head and looked at David and nodded. Then he started coughing.

"The doctor will come by and take a look at you. Just relax. You're coughing because of the smoke. It'll be alright."

Neil coughed, nodded again then closed his eyes.

David walked to the next gurney, and repeated the process for Sarah. She had more burns and blisters on her face, so David took great care in placing the mask on her. She began to cough after a couple of breaths.

"Can you roll over onto your side, Mrs. Ritter? We don't want you to choke." David reached down to help her. With great effort, Sarah tried to roll over. She stopped twice from the pain.

"Take your time, ma'am. I know it hurts. But we don't want you to choke."

Sarah finally made it to her right side, despite the pain, and looked up at David. He patted her head.

"Doctor Goodson will be here as soon as he can to look at you, okay ma'am?"

Sarah nodded and closed her eyes.

David walked down to Orville, who was already on his side and wheezing. His eyes, blood red and dilated, didn't appear to be focusing on anything. His face, still black with red splotches, showed signs of swelling, especially around his eyes and mouth.

Oh my God. I needed to put oxygen on him first.

David didn't wait to try to exchange pleasantries. He quickly put the oxygen mask on Orville.

"Breathe for me, sir. Try to take some deep breaths. This is oxygen for you sir." David said loudly.

I'm not sure if he can hear me. Goodson needs to get over here quickly.

David ran over to Mildred, who was at the nurses' station talking in low tones with another nurse.

"Nurse Hodges?" David interrupted, "I'm sorry, ma'am, but I'm concerned about the old guy in the hall. His eyes look bad. His breathing, it isn't good. I'm not sure he's completely conscious."

Mildred looked toward the hallway.

"Thank you, David. I appreciate you getting the oxygen started. I'll find Doctor Goodson and let him know what you saw." Mildred nodded as she took off looking for the doctor.

5:28 a.m.
Kraft Foods, Springfield, Missouri

Norman received the news of the fire first. He worked the night maintenance shift at the Kraft Foods plant in Springfield. His wife Jerry called, asking for him to be paged for an emergency.

"What is it, dear? You… you never call here… at this hour." Norman sounded out of breath from running.

"Norman, honey, I got a call from Modena Pitts in Ava. Honey, there's been a fire at the house. Your mom and dad, Neil, and Virginia are on their way to St. John's right now. They're hurt bad. Dewey…"

Jerry's voice cracked as she began to cry.

"Dewey and the baby… they didn't make it out of the house…"

"What?" Norman couldn't believe his ears.

"Modena said…everyone… everyone had to jump… out of the windows on the second floor," Jerry cried as she spoke. "She said Dewey… Dewey pushed Virginia out the window… then… then they said… they said… Oh God, Norman… he was holding Gary… and the floor collapsed under him. They… they didn't make it out. Dewey's dead, Norman. He and little Gary… they died in the fire." She was crying too hard to speak further.

"Jesus. I didn't even get to see him. He can't be gone!" Norman said, rubbing his forehead.

"I know, honey. I'm so sorry," Jerry sniffed.

"Jerry, can you call everyone else? I don't think I can do it. I'll talk to my boss and get out of here, and head over to St. John's." Norman fought back tears.

Dammit, I never even got to see him when he got back. Dammit!

"Of course, love, I'll call everyone. Norman, honey, be careful driving over there."

"I will."

"Norman?"

"Yes."

"I love you. I'm so sorry."

"Thank you, honey. I love you too. I'm gonna get out of here and head over."

"Okay."

Within two minutes, Norman was in his Ford Mainline, pulling out of the driveway of the employee parking lot, and driving to St. John's. Speeding through the quiet streets of Springfield, Norman's mind barely focused on driving as he thought about the news.

How can Dewey be gone? I didn't even get to see him. I didn't get to see any of them. The house is gone? Drafty old place. Wonder how the fire started. They had to jump? How did Dad manage to jump? How did anyone catch him? How badly are they hurt?

Once parked in the hospital parking lot, Norman ran to the emergency room lobby. Rounding the corner, he stopped in his tracks when he saw the room filled with sick and hurt people waiting for their turn to be seen by the doctor. Breathing hard, he stepped quickly over to the nurse seated behind the check-in desk.

"May I help you?" her tiny voice squeaked as she strained to look at him, his large frame towering over her.

"Yes, ma'am, my name is Norman Ritter. I was told that my mother, father, brother, and sister-in-law are here. They were in a fire in Ava."

"Ohhhhh, the burn victims," she said, looking at her clipboard. "Yes, Mr. Ritter, they arrived a short time ago. They are still being tended to."

"Can I see them?" Norman inquired.

"Not yet, sir, I'm sorry. The doctor hasn't gotten to all of them yet so you can't go back there. If you can have a seat, I'll check and let you know when you can go back there."

"Thank you, ma'am." Norman nodded, stepping away from the desk. Looking around, he found a chair in the corner to wait.

Seated only a few minutes, Norman looked up to see his brother Ray running in. At 26, Ray was a student at Southwest Missouri State University in Springfield and married with two children. Norman got up to greet him. The two brothers shook hands then hugged, slapping each other hard on the back the way men do when they don't know how else to show affection.

"What the hell happened, Norman?" Ray inquired after the back slapping ended.

"I don't really know much of anything yet." Norman sighed as they sat down beside each other. “Apparently the house caught fire this morning, and they couldn’t get down the stairs. Jerry said Virginia is hurt bad, and everyone else is burned pretty bad. They had to jump out the windows.”

“Jerry said Dewey and Gary didn’t make it out,” Ray said with his head down.

“Yep, that’s what I was told.”

“Damn.”

“Yep.”

Both men sighed and didn’t say anything for a few minutes.

As the two were sitting there, heads down in silence, Delmas walked in.

When he got the news, Delbert called his girlfriend Dorothy Moody to let her know.

“I’m leaving right now to head to the emergency room.”

“Come pick me up, Delbert. I want to be there with you,” Dorothy insisted.

“Are you sure? This won’t be a pleasant visit,” Delbert argued.

“I know. Come get me.”

After Delbert picked up Dorothy and arrived at the hospital, being so preoccupied with the situation, he led Dorothy down a wrong hallway and they ended up in the middle of the emergency room.

“Here, Delbert, the waiting room is out here. Let’s see who’s there,” Dorothy said, pulling Delbert by the hand. They walked down Hall 2, and failed to pay close attention to the blackened people lying on gurneys against the wall, waiting for attention. Neil, Sarah, and Orville were still waiting to be seen, with oxygen masks on, and Delbert didn’t recognize them when he and Dorothy walked past them.

6:37 a.m.
Waiting Room, St. John’s Emergency Room

Virginia’s parents, Garland and Lula Dye, along with their son Donnal, walked into the waiting room, bewildered with red, swollen eyes from crying. Norman was the first to see them and got up to greet them.

"Hello, Garland," Norman said, wrapping his big arms around his friend. The rest of the siblings stopped their conversations to see who had arrived. Dorothy got up from her chair and walked over to hug Lula.

"We got here as fast as we could," Garland said, pulling away after hugging Norman, "Do you know anything? Has anyone seen them?"

"Afraid not." Norman shook his head. "They are still working on Virginia apparently, and no word yet on Mom, Dad, and Neil."

Garland grabbed Norman's arm as the other brothers drew near.

"Is it true, Norman? Did Dewey and Gary not make it out?"

Delbert moved forward and put his arm around Garland.

"Yeah. It's true, Garland." Norman sighed and lowered his head.

Garland hung his head, huge tears running down his cheeks and dripping onto the floor.

"I loved Dewey, you guys," Garland said, trying to address whoever was around him, "I loved... loved your brother as if he was my own son… And that little Gary… Oh God!"

Norman pulled Garland into him as he began to sob. Dorothy was already holding Lula, the two women crying together. Delbert leaned in from behind Garland and wrapped his arms around Donnal. Everyone else stood around them in silence. The entire waiting room began to notice the family, as people began to talk around the room about the people whose house had burned and a little boy who had died in the fire. Eventually the spectators hushed, watching the entire family circle around the Dyes as they wept. In one massive huddle, the entire group cried together.

8

5:15 a.m.
Dye Residence, Ava, Missouri

As he watched the Dyes pull out of their driveway, Sheriff Souder looked at his watch.

Gonna be a long day...

Just then his stomach growled, reminding him that he had been up since receiving the call about the fire just before 3:00. He got back in his patrol car, drove into town, and did a quick lap around the Ava square to make sure everything looked secure, then headed north on Jefferson Street, pulling into the parking lot at the Highway House Café.

A cold north wind still blew when Sheriff Souder walked into the diner, shaking off the chill. Ben, behind the counter, greeted him from across the room.

"Hey, Sheriff! Pull up a stool! Care for some coffee?"

"You bet, Ben. Better make it black."

Ben poured coffee, eyeballing the sheriff as he took a seat on one of the stools at the counter.

"A little unusual for you to drink your coffee black, Don. What's up?"

"Been up since just before 3:00."

"Couldn't sleep?" He began wiping down the counter.

"I wish." Don slurped his coffee. "You know Orville Ritter and his bunch?"

"Of course! He's related to some of my kin way back."

Don took another slurp.

"Well, there was a bad fire there early this morning. Orville's hurt bad, so is his wife, Sarah. Their boy Neil woke them up to discover the house was on fire."

Ben's eyes widened.

"The worst of it," Don continued, "their boy Dewey had just gotten home from the Air Force a few days back. Him and his wife Virginia and their little boy Gary."

"Yep, I heard they made it back to town but I hadn't seen them yet."

"Well, they were staying there. Dewey and the little boy didn't make it out."

"Oh my god!" Ben scowled. "What about Virginia?"

"Dewey pushed her out the window before he went down. She's hurt bad. Pregnant, too. I don't know, Ben, one helluva way to start the day."

Don took another sip.

"Jesus, Sheriff! Did they lose everything?"

"Everything." Don nodded. "Clinkingbeard is on-site right now, waiting for the place to cool down so that he can recover the bodies. One of the neighbors is going to help."

"God, that's awful. I'm going to let Elaine know so that she can get word out to the ladies of the church."

"Good idea. They're going to need a lot of help."

"Do you want something to eat, Don?" Ben continued wiping down the counter.

"Yeah, I need to eat something. Give me whatever your special is."

After finishing his breakfast, Don reached back to get his wallet, but Ben waved him off.

"This one's on me, Don. Where you headed next?"

"Thanks buddy. I gotta go see Dick Ritter, to tell him the news." Don sighed, "I hate to do it. It's the worst part of my job when something like this happens. Already had to tell the Dyes what happened. Now I gotta tell Dick."

"I know it'll be tough on them. Tell Dick and Cora that Elaine and I will be praying for the family."

Don nodded then headed back into the cold morning.

One of the households hardest hit by the news was that of Orville's younger brother, Richard "Dick" Ritter. Tall, handsome, athletic and friendly, Dick was loved and respected by the entire town of Ava. Eight and a half years younger than Orville, he was especially fond of his older brother and the two grew up as close as if they had been twins. He lived north of town, near the spot where the first post office had been erected for the community during the Civil War.

Pulling into the driveway, Sheriff Souder saw a light on in the kitchen window.

"Well at least they are up and around already," Souder said out loud, relieved to know he wasn't going to have to wake them up like he had to with the Dyes. Don and Dick had been friends for years, hunted together, and like the rest of the family, were on a first-name basis with each other.

"In all the years I've known Dick, this will be the first time I've had to deliver news like this," Souder muttered as he parked his car and walked toward the door.

6:05 a.m.
Bollinger Residence, Seymour, Missouri

Speedy and Wanda Bollinger had been living in their new brick home on the south side of Seymour just one week and did not have a telephone yet. Speedy, already awake and getting dressed to open his café for the morning, was startled to hear frantic pounding on the door. The noise awakened Wanda, and she grabbed a robe as Speedy ran to answer the door. There, pale and disheveled, stood Paul Triplett from the local funeral home. Clarence Clinkingbeard called him from Paul Pitts' house when he stepped away from the scene and asked Triplett to let the Bollingers know what happened.

"Good lord, Paul, what in the world has got you out this time of mornin'?" Speedy asked, motioning for Paul to enter the living room.

Just as Paul started to speak, Wanda entered the room, still messing with the sash on her robe.

"Good mornin', Miss Wanda, Speedy. Sorry to bother so early. I need to talk with both of you…"

7:00 a.m.
Ritter Farmhouse Site, Ava, Missouri

Elga walked to the back of the area where the house once stood, with two pairs of work gloves that he had taken from his truck. Clarence, standing with his hands on his hips, stared into the wreckage and smoking remains of the house, unaware of Elga's approach.

"Do you see them, Clarence?"

Clarence jumped, startled out of his thoughts.

"Reckon you might want some gloves." Elga tried to smile as he handed Clarence a pair. "It's likely to be a bit warm in there."

"Thank you, Elga." Clarence smiled as he took the gloves. "It's still too hot in there to go in. But yes. I can see the child."

"Where?" Elga stared into the smoldering rubble.

"There." Clarence pointed at a pile of rubble in the cellar area about four feet away from the outer wall. "See that section that looks like a piece of a cabinet?"

"Yep." Elga nodded.

"Underneath that. The little boy's head."

"Jesus…" Elga looked away.

"I don't see the airman though."

Elga didn't look back.

"I know this will be tough, Elga, but I appreciate your assistance. I just can't do it alone."

"I know, Clarence. I know…" Elga put his hands in his pockets and stared at the orange and pink colors of the sky as the sun rose.

7:22 a.m.

As Elga tried to prepare himself for the recovery effort, the Ava school bus drove by, slowly trudging its way up the hill on Hunter Road. Inside the bus, Elga's daughter, eight-year-old Sharon Vinson, noticed the smoldering mass where the house once stood.

"Where's the house? What happened to the people that lived there?" she called out to her friends. Soon the bus was buzzing with questions, all the children wondering what happened there.

8:32 a.m.

Elga stood by his truck and waved when the fire truck made its way down the driveway to Hunter Road. He looked down at his watch.

"Must be time to do this," he sighed.

Walking toward the remains of the house, he saw Clarence pacing, gloved hands clasped tightly behind his back. Clarence stopped pacing when he caught sight of Elga walking toward him.

"It appears the fire truck has run dry." Clarence nodded at Elga. "They said they would return when they refill. I believe it is cool enough in there. We should be able to do our task, carefully of course."

"Yep," Elga nodded. "Let's get this done."

"It appears this is some sort of cellar below the kitchen." Clarence pointed as they approached.

"Yep, sure is. Orville and his boys dug out this cellar when they redid the outside of this house. It's about four feet deep or so."

"Watch your step, Elga."

The two men stepped gingerly through the warm rubble, making their way into the area where earlier Clarence had seen Gary's head.

As Clarence leaned over to pull debris away from that area, Elga stopped him.

"Clarence, I feel like I kinda need to prepare myself for what I'm gonna see here."

"I understand." Clarence smiled weakly. "Elga, it won't be pleasant. This house burned at a temperature of about 1100 degrees, roughly. That's the general temperature at which most wood burns, so I figure that's a decent estimate. When a body is cremated, the furnace is run at about 1800 degrees for several hours to break down the materials of the body. Since the house burned at a temperature below that of cremation but still very hot, my suspicion is that we will find relatively complete bodies in very bad condition. It wasn't hot enough to turn them to ashes."

Elga sighed.

"Okay. I guess it's now or never." Elga held his breath as the two men leaned over and began to lift pieces of debris and partially burned wood.

"Be careful, Elga," Clarence warned, "I noticed some of this is still quite warm. I sure appreciate the gloves."

After about 10 minutes of carefully removing the rubble, Elga let out a gasp.

"I think I just uncovered something, Clarence." Elga began to tremble.

Clarence leaned over to closely inspect the shape that Elga had uncovered.

"I'm afraid you are correct, Elga. Let's concentrate our efforts right here and recover these souls."

The bodies were buried in a few inches of embers and debris, about five feet apart. Elga and Clarence worked quickly to uncover them then stood up.

Before them lay the barely recognizable black masses of an adult and child. The adult's right arm was missing, but the left arm clearly folded inward. The adult's head was tilted back, like it was looking toward the back wall, its escape route. The child was on its side, just a small mass with no legs or arms.

The sight was too much for Elga, and tears rolled down his face.

"Dear God. They were so close to each other, so close to the edge of the house," he gasped.

Clarence put his hand on Elga's shoulder as he wept. Neither of them moved for several minutes.

9

October 27, 12:28 p.m.
Waiting Room, St. John's Emergency Room

Dr. Charles Lockhart paused and looked at his watch before walking into the waiting room.

It's been a long day already. It's been even longer for these folks, bless 'em.

With a deep sigh, he turned the corner and stepped in. Being a tall, slender man in his mid-30s, with jet-black hair and a clean-shaven face, his entrance caught the attention of everyone in the room, and he found himself staring back at twenty pairs of eyes.

"I need to speak with everyone in the Ritter family, please."

Fifteen arms went up. They occupied half of the waiting room, sprawled out on couches and chairs. Lockhart grabbed an open chair near the family as everyone crowded in close to hear what he had to say.

"Folks, I wanted to give you an update on how everyone is doing. My name is Doctor Charles Lockhart, and I'm the attending physician for your family members since they arrived this morning. Here it is early afternoon now, and we've moved them to regular rooms and have gotten a good look at how each person is doing and responding. So that's why I'm here to talk with you and see if you have any questions.

First, Neil. His burns were not too severe, just some broad first-degree burns across his face and scalp, plus blisters and a gash in a small area on his forehead. We talked with him about that spot, and he said that's where a flaming beam hit him when the second floor collapsed. He's going to have a scar there for quite some time. Who knows, he may always have that scar. His feet were pretty cut up from running on the road and a bit burned as well, but those are going to be fine. He's also dehydrated. They're all dehydrated, as a matter of fact. We have all of them on IV."

Lockhart took in a breath.

"But back to Neil specifically, he's been having horrible flashbacks to the fire. All morning. He's been breaking down and crying off and on throughout the day."

"All day?" Wanda asked.

"Yes, I'm afraid so. He's greatly distressed by it. We hear about this type of thing often, when something dramatic happens, and the memories of the event won't go away. Usually with something like this, people go into what is commonly called shock. It's the brain's way of protecting itself. Memories of a traumatic event are effectively erased, allowing the person to cope more easily. But Neil does not appear to have experienced shock and thus remembers everything. It happens occasionally. This is one of the most intense cases of it I've ever seen. But apparently he heard and saw things that were pretty awful."

"Doctor," Norman's wife Jerry spoke up, "can you tell us what he's been saying?"

"Yes," Doctor Lockhart agreed, nodding toward her. "Our nurses report that it appears that he and his mother were trying to get to this brother…"

"Dewey," several voices chimed in.

"…Dewey," Doctor Lockhart nodded, "and could not reach him. The fact that he couldn't save him and couldn't get to him are causing him great distress. Apparently as he died, Dewey was screaming for Neil to come help him. They all heard him screaming."

Wanda gasped.

"Physically he is going to be fine," Doctor Lockhart continued, "and we expect to release him after a week or so. But he is bearing some emotional scars, and may need something more than we can offer. I'm referring to psychiatric help."

Norman, Delmas and Delbert looked at each other.

"Next, I'd like to update you on Virginia. Are her parents present?" Doctor Lockhart looked around the room.

"We are her parents," Garvin Dye spoke up, still holding Lula closely.

"Okay. Well, as you may know, Virginia was hurt pretty badly when she fell. She's going to take some time to heal. She broke her pelvis on impact, but there are no other broken bones. She hurt her arm and ankle in the fall, and she's bruised and very sore in a lot of places, but she's going to be okay. Bed rest is best in her circumstance, and I foresee that we will get her healed up to a certain point, then will ultimately release her to convalesce. I assume we will release her to you?"

"Yes, of course." Garland nodded, looking at Lula then the doctor. "She'll come home with us to heal up."

"Good." Lockhart smiled. "I see such release taking place within just a few short weeks."

"Doctor Lockhart," Dorothy spoke up, "we've heard that Virginia might have been pregnant. Is she okay? I mean, is her baby okay?"

"You are correct, she was pregnant, and she told the staff that she was. But the impact was too great, and the baby didn't survive. There was no fetal heartbeat when we checked."

Lula let out a gasp as Garland turned to pull her in closer to him. She buried her head in his shirt and began to cry loudly.

"Does she know, Doctor?" Dorothy asked, her eyes tearing up.

"Yes. I told her."

Everyone was quiet for a moment.

"Something else about her, so that you all are aware. She believes that the loss of Dewey and the little boy…"

"Gary."

"…Gary and additionally this unborn child are all her fault. She has told a couple of nurses that if she hadn't delayed jumping out the window, Dewey would have survived."

Everyone shook their heads, while Norman spoke up, "No, of course that's not true, Doctor."

"Well, I would tend to agree, Mr. Ritter," Doctor Lockhart nodded. "But none of us can convince her of that. I only bring it up so that perhaps you all can reassure her while you visit. Don't overwhelm her with it. But be ready to respond if it comes up. We must be very careful with her. She may be a suicide risk. So please watch what you say and how you say it."

Everyone in the room nodded.

"Moving on to Sarah," the doctor continued, "she has been burned quite severely. She has large third-degree burns on her shoulder, down her arm, and on her leg. The rest of her body, especially her face, is burned as well, and she has several large blisters, but these other burns I just mentioned, while quite painful, are only first and second degree and should heal nicely. The shoulder, arm and leg are considerably more challenging due to the extent of tissue damage. But we will do all we can. We are going to have to keep her heavily sedated to control the pain. When you spend time with her, she may lapse in and out of semi consciousness."

Everyone nodded silently.

"What about Dad, Doctor?" Ray spoke up.

"I was saving a discussion about him for last." The doctor sighed after a long pause. "I wish I had better news, but Orville is in very bad condition. His burns are quite bad. Not as bad as Sarah's, but they are severe. Third degree in a couple of places on his arms and legs, the rest first and second degree, including his feet, face, and scalp. But the biggest problem is his smoke inhalation. The thick hot smoke laced with toxins from construction materials essentially turned his lungs into paper. The telltale signs of this are the swelling that we see in his face and the discoloring of the skin, aside from the obvious blackening caused by the fire and soot. His lungs quit processing the oxygen properly within minutes of inhaling all that smoke, and unfortunately with no oxygen on site, damage began quickly. He was barely conscious when he arrived at our emergency room. Now, unfortunately, with the reduced oxygen flow, we believe there has been some significant, irreversible damage to the brain."

Everyone in the room gasped, and Wanda hid her face in her hands.

"I'm sorry, I know that's terrible news. But I feel I need to explain it straight to all of you. Now…" the doctor continued, "…we have a high probability of pneumonia settling into his damaged lungs as well. Without the ability to sit up and cough and move around, the pneumonia will continue to consume his lungs unabated. It doesn't look good for him at all."

"Doctor Lockhart," Norman spoke up without raising his head, "it sounds to me like you are trying to tell us that our dad is dying."

"Yes, Mr. Ritter. I'm afraid that's correct."

"How long do you think he's got?"

"Well, it's tough to judge, but honestly I don't believe he is going to live through the weekend. We can only do our best to keep him comfortable. He may never regain consciousness."

Everyone in the room, except Norman, Ray, Delbert, and Delmas, began to cry. Delbert and Delmas stared at the floor. Ray quickly wiped a tear from his eye as Norman kept his head lowered.

After several seconds, Doctor Lockhart spoke up again.

"One other thing, with this large of a family, I need to ask if there is one of you who can serve as the family representative, so that there is only one point of contact for any unpleasant or official family business that needs to be handled in the next few days. It would just make things flow much more easily."

"That would be me, Doctor." Norman quickly stood up. "I'm Norman, I'm the oldest. I can certainly be your contact man and can make any decisions on behalf of the family." Norman leaned forward to shake hands with the doctor.

"Thank you, Norman." Charles nodded, stepping over to shake hands. "I appreciate it. If we don't have your phone number on file, please make sure it gets added." He turned to Garland, who was still comforting Lula. "Mr. Dye, I need your contact information as well, so that we can continue to talk about Virginia."

Garland nodded.

Doctor Lockhart returned his attention to the entire family. "Again, I'm sorry to be the bearer of bad news. It means a lot to have all of you here. These people are going to need you over these next few rough days and weeks, and you'll need each other. Please feel free to contact me if you have any questions. Oh, and here are their room numbers, if someone can write this down…"

Jerry, Wanda, Barbara, Margaret, and Dorothy all scrambled for paper in their purses. Doctor Lockhart waited until all of them had paper and a pen and looked back up at him.

"They are all on 4 West. That's the fourth floor, west wing. Neil is in 420. Virginia is in 401. Sarah is in 412. And Orville is in 425."

"Thank you, Doctor." Norman choked back tears.

Doctor Lockhart looked around the room and nodded at the others still looking at him. He turned quickly and left the room.

After a lengthy silence, Norman spoke up.

"Do any of you ladies have another sheet of paper and a pen?"

After all the ladies rummaged through their purses again, Ray's wife Barbara held up a sheet of paper and pen and passed it to Norman.

"I think we need to plan when we can be here, to watch over Mom. And it sounds like we better look in on Virginia if we can."

"What about Neil?" Dorothy asked.

"Sounds like Neil is getting out in a few days," Norman said without looking up.

"But the doctor said he's hurting so badly and having nightmares." Wanda sniffled, raising a tissue to wipe her nose.

"Sounds to me like Neil just needs to get over it…" Delmas grumbled.

"We can all drop in on Neil, too," Norman raised his voice, interrupting Delmas, as he began scribbling. "But Mom needs us the worst. And I think we all need to say to Dad whatever we need to say. Sounds like he may not know we are there, but we should at least try. Here, write your names and what times you can be here."

Norman looked up and made eye contact with Delmas.

"Cool it, little brother. You weren't there," Norman growled quietly.

After Norman collected the schedule with the times at which everyone could visit the hospital, he stood up, towering over everyone.

"Okay folks, sounds like we can finally go see them. Let's get up there."

He looked at the Dyes, who still had tears in their eyes.

"Garland and Lula, none of us are going to come in and see Virginia until you've had plenty of time with her," Norman declared. "She needs you two pretty bad right now. We'll wait."

"Okay, Norman, thank you." Garland smiled weakly as Lula

gathered up her coat and purse.

In a mass of coats and purses, the family gathered up their belongings and in almost complete silence made their way down the hall to the elevators. Both elevators opened at once, and the entire group managed to land on the fourth floor of the west wing at the same time. Still in silence, the Ritters split to find the rooms for Neil, Sarah, and Orville, as the Dyes headed to Room 401 to see their daughter.

10

1:07 p.m.
St. John's Hospital, Room 420, Springfield, Missouri

Margaret, along with Speedy and Wanda found Room 420 quickly. Upon opening the door, they found Neil lying with his bed propped up, his head turned away from the door, staring blankly out the window.

Margaret gently tapped on the heavy wood door and softly called out, "Neil?"

Neil turned and eyes widened as he saw her step quickly toward him, followed more slowly by Speedy and Wanda. Speedy smiled from over Wanda's shoulder and whispered, "Hey, little brother."

Neil burst into tears as Margaret leaned down over him. He threw his arms around her and sobbed while she held him.

"Oh, honey, it's okay," Margaret whispered, "It's gonna be okay, Neil."

Neil tried to speak between sobs.

"Oh my God, sis… it was awful… Dewey… he screamed… I couldn't get to him… Mom tried too…"

Neil's cries got louder as he tried to talk.

"I can't… He won't stop screaming… I can still hear him screaming… He… He burned! Burned alive! Oh God, sis! I can't! Oh, I just can't!"

Margaret held Neil for several minutes as he sobbed uncontrollably into her chest, pounding his fist on the bed. Wanda sat down on the bed while Speedy stood beside her, his hand on her back. She leaned over onto Neil as he cried against Margaret. After several minutes, Wanda tearfully turned back and looked up at Speedy towering over her.

"My God, honey," she mouthed to him, shaking her head.

1:07 p.m.
St. John's Hospital, Room 412

Norman and Jerry, along with Ray and Barbara, found Room 412 where Sarah lay unconscious. A nurse was checking her IV tube as they walked into the room.

"Are you family?"

"Yes, ma'am, we are." Norman nodded.

"She's heavily medicated because of the pain. You can talk to her, but she may not respond. The doctor said her lungs sound pretty good, and her heartbeat is regular. So she's doing okay, all things considered. Please let me know if you need something."

"Thank you, Nurse," Ray spoke up.

"Oh, one other thing." The nurse stopped before leaving the room. "Please refrain from touching her. Her burns are bad, and we have them dressed, but it's very painful, even in her sedated state."

"Okay, thank you," Jerry said as Norman and Ray moved to either side of her bed. Jerry and Barbara stood at the foot of the bed, watching their husbands get a first look at their mother, covered with blisters and scorched red from the fire.

Norman knelt down beside Sarah's ear.

"Momma? Momma, it's Norman. Just wanted to let you know I'm here, with Jerry, Ray, and Barbara. The whole family is here, Momma. You're going to be okay. We're all here with you. Love you, Momma."

In her sedated state, Sarah let out a long sigh, and cleared her throat in a long, hard, festering growl.

"Maybe she heard you, big brother." Ray winked at Norman, then leaned over beside her other ear.

"Hey, Mom, it's Ray. Don't you worry none, ever'thing is gonna be okay. Rest, Mom. I love you."

Sarah's feet twitched under the sheet. Jerry and Barbara, standing at the end of the bed, looked at each other, then lifted the sheet to get a look at her feet. They both let out a gasp when they saw her red, swollen, burned feet, from being barefoot on the burning floor before she jumped out the window.

"Norman, honey, come look." Jerry reached out to her husband. Norman stepped to the end of the bed while Barbara motioned for Ray to do the same. Both men cringed as they saw their mother's burned feet.

"Jesus, that floor must have been on fire when they were getting ready to jump," Ray whispered.

"Damn," Norman echoed.

Barbara gently laid the sheet back over Sarah's feet. No one said anything for a moment. They just stood there and watched Sarah sleep.

Norman looked around, noticing the single chairs on either side of his mother's bed.

"Let's get some more chairs in here," he directed.

1:07 p.m.
St. John's Hospital, Room 425

At Room 425, Delmas, Mary, Delbert, and Dorothy found the door closed. The twins looked at each other, then Delbert slowly pushed the door open to peek inside. Noticing that no one else was in the room except Orville, he opened the door and nodded at the other three.

The chilly room, with its heat turned completely off caused Mary and Dorothy to stop and put on their coats. With drapes drawn and the ceiling lights dim, the sight of the room's single unconscious occupant made the four visitors draw in their breath.

Orville lay flat on his back, barely covered with a sheet. His face, swollen with splotches of red and yellow, twitched occasionally as everyone stood looking.

"My God, it doesn't hardly look like him," Delmas whispered.

"No, it doesn't," Delbert whispered back, choking back tears.

Moving forward, the foursome stood around Orville's bed in silence. Mary reached over and gently grasped Delmas' hand.

"I don't even know what to say to him," Delbert said, barely above a whisper.

"We need to try to say something to him. Just in case he can hear," Dorothy whispered.

Delmas slipped to one side of Orville's bed, followed by Mary, while Delbert and Dorothy moved to the other side. The twins leaned over their dad's head.

"Dad?" Delmas struggled to find words. "Dad, it's Delmas. I don't know what to say right now… Just wanted to let you know we are here. We're all here."

"Hey, old man." Delbert grinned. "We are here for you buddy. Don't go chasing the nurses around here. They don't look kindly on that."

Dorothy and Mary cracked a smile despite their tears.

Orville breathed in then let out a muffled "Mmmmmfffffffff."

Delbert looked up at Delmas, wide-eyed.

"He might have heard that." Delbert smiled.

After several minutes of silence with no one moving, Delbert reached over and ran his fingers through the patchy hair on Orville's head, much of it burned off when his clothes caught fire just before he jumped. Several areas of scalp were red and blistered.

"God, I hate to think of what he went through before he jumped," Mary whispered.

1:07 p.m.
St. John's Hospital, Room 401

Garland, Lula, and Donnal Dye walked hand in hand down the hall to Room 401, breathing deeply as they approached the room. The door was open, so Lula stepped in ahead of Garland and Donnal, gasping when they saw Virginia lying flat on her back in the bed with her head turned toward the window. Hearing the gasp, Virginia turned toward the door, bursting into tears when she saw her parents rushing toward her. Reaching up, she wrapped her arms tightly around her mother as Lula leaned down to hold her.

"Oh, Momma!" Virginia sobbed as Lula held her. Garland walked around Lula and leaned over, patting Virginia on her shoulder to let her know he was there. Donnal sat down in the chair next to the bed.

Virginia tried to speak amidst her sobs.

"Momma... Daddy... Oh God! Oh God, it was awful! My Dewey... Gary...they're both gone! I... I lost... I lost this baby, too... I... couldn't... I was scared... Oh, Momma... Momma... It's... my fault... I should... I should have jumped... sooner... Oh, God!"

"Shhhh, baby, shhhh, it's going to be alright. It's not your fault, honey," Lula tried to comfort Virginia, who was by now sobbing uncontrollably.

"Honey, it's okay. You did the best you could," Garland jumped in, "Sweetheart, it was a scary thing. You couldn't have known... you couldn't have known it would turn out this way."

"Oh, Daddy... I was... I was... so... scared," Virginia sobbed. "Oh, Daddy he's gone. My... my Dewey is gone... and my babies... are gone!"

As the three of them cried together, Donnal lowered his head and began to cry too.

"I can't believe they're gone," Donnal said quietly. "Dewey was such a neat guy."

Garland turned to see his son crying.

"Come here, son. Don't sit over there and cry by yourself. Come here."

Donnal got up and leaned over against his dad as Garland wrapped his arm around him.

A nurse stepped into the room to check on Virginia. Stopping when she saw the family huddled together, she stepped back quietly into the hall, closing the door to let them weep privately. They never knew she was there, crying together in one prolonged, grieving wail.

1:10 p.m.
Gloria Bailey Residence, Ava, Missouri

That afternoon in the town of Ava, several ladies of the local Good Neighbors Club settled into Gloria Bailey's dining room for their monthly meeting. Before the meeting was called to order, however, talk of the family tragedy filled the room.

"You know they lost everything in that fire." Gloria shook her head. "That little ole shack must have gone up like a matchstick."

"I heard the young father and his little boy died in the flames." Esther Beaumister teared up. "They couldn't get out, poor dears."

"You know, that Dewey Ritter repaired a radio for me back when he had his little electronics shop off the square," Mrs. Sharp announced, shaking her head with the other ladies. "He certainly was a handsome thing."

The talk continued until Gloria called the meeting to order. It was customary for the ladies to suspend their meetings after October until the following spring, so they took care of that point of business quickly. After the vote, Zola Allen raised her hand.

"Gloria," Zola rose to speak. "Since we are suspending our meetings as usual until the spring, and in light of the horrible tragedy that has struck the Ritter family, I would like to make a motion that we donate our current treasury to the relief fund for the family. There are many people and organizations that are beginning to collect money, and I think it would be proper in the spirit of our Good Neighbor Club to donate what we have to the family."

As Zola sat down, Gloria took over.

"Thank you, Zola. We have a motion on the floor, is there any discussion?"

Several ladies muttered, "I agree" and "Good idea" to one another as Gloria looked around the room for comments. A second was voiced, the vote taken, and the motion passed. With all business concluded, the ladies shifted their attention to tea and games.

By Wednesday evening, church services throughout Ava and the surrounding area took special offerings for the family and held prayer vigils for the four victims in the hospital in Springfield.

11

October 28, 2:32 a.m.
St. John's Hospital, Room 425

"Dad?"

Neil walked slowly into the dark room.

"Dad?"

"Hmmft."

"Dad, it's Neil."

"Mmff uuh pfff tmm."

Neil sat down in the chair next to Orville's bed to better hear his father's sedative-induced mumblings.

"Dad, I'm guessing you're in there. I hope you can sorta hear me."

He slipped his hand into Orville's hand. Orville's body quivered for a moment.

"Dad, I just wanted to tell you I'm sorry. I'm… I'm sorry that I stayed out so late that night. I'm sorry… that I didn't wake up sooner. Maybe… maybe Dewey and Gary would still be alive if I had woke up sooner. You… You wouldn't be laying here dying… I'm… I'm sorry I couldn't get to Dewey…"

He stopped and wiped the tears streaming down his face.

"Oh, Dad… I wish… I wish we could go back to that day. Things would be different. We'd all be together. We'd all be okay."

"Mmmmf… buhhh mmm pumf."

"You… you just lay here and rest, old man. I won't pester you anymore."

Neil was about to pull his hand away when Orville's grip suddenly tightened. Orville continued to squeeze as Neil's eyes widened. After a few seconds, Orville's grip loosened again and Neil pulled his hand back.

"You still got a strong grip there, feller."

"Mffpt."

"Just rest now Dad," Neil whispered, struggling to his feet, "I love you."

Neil turned to walk out the door.

"Muh hff u tuh."

Startled, Neil turned quickly to look back and see if Orville was conscious.

Did he just tell me he loved me too? Is that even possible?

Neil stepped back to Orville's bed and looked down closely at the figure laying there.

"Dad? Are you awake?"

Silence, except the sound of Orville's shallow breathing.

Neil smiled, turned, and shuffled out the door with his head down.

12

On Thursday, October 29, the Douglas County Herald ran a front-page story on the fire, telling the tale of Dewey and Gary falling to their deaths. Trying to provide as many details as possible, the reporter noted that Dewey's last words to Virginia were "I'm burning up alive!" The quickly penned story then continued to erroneously describe Neil getting in his car (Neil didn't have a car at the house) and driving to George Pledger's place, with further info of summoning neighbors. According to the story, only bones were found during the recovery of Dewey and Gary, and that they were found intermingled, which countered an earlier story in which Clarence Clinkingbeard reported that he saw the body of the child some time before they could get into the wreckage to recover both casualties. The story also reported that a wood stove and fuel oil stove were burning downstairs and theorized that one or both started the fire.

At Ava Drug, Doc Gentry found a large glass jar, made a sign "Donations for Ritter family", and set it by the cash register at the soda fountain. Herman King at Ava Hardware set up a similar collection jar with the article from the Herald nearby so that anyone who needed could read more about the fire.

October 29, 11:48 a.m.
Hungry House Café, Ava, Missouri

Sheriff Souder sat at the counter sipping coffee while Clyde Huff and Steven Lakey sat in a nearby booth discussing the article about the fire in the Herald.

"They shouldn't oughta print stories with that much detail." Clyde shook his head.

"How come? People got a right to know what's happened to their neighbors!" Steven argued.

"Yeah, but there's just too much detail here. It's not proper."

"They gotta tell the story, Clyde."

"I'm betting they made half of this up, to make it sound better."

Souder spun around on his seat and looked at the two men.

"No, they didn't!" Souder barked, "I'm not sure about a couple of those details, but they wouldn't try to make it sound better."

Huff and Lakey turned quickly in their seats as Souder got up from his stool, walked over to the table and leaned down to face the two men.

"I was there, gentlemen. One of the first on the scene." Souder looked at Huff then Lakey. "In all my years of doing this, I've never seen anything so awful. Don't ever want to again, neither."

Huff and Lakey looked at each other then back at Souder.

"We didn't mean nothing by it, Sheriff." Lakey shrugged.

Souder looked down then patted Lakey on the shoulder.

"I know. I'm sorry, boys. It's just… well… it was awful. That's all I can say. It was awful."

12:10 p.m.
St. John's Hospital, Room 412

Norman struggled to stay awake sitting next to Sarah's bed, keeping vigil over her as she slipped in and out of consciousness. The sound of her breathing deeply, coupled with the fact that he had put in a full shift at work overnight, caught up with him, and his eyelids grew heavy.

Just as he began to nod off, Ray walked into the room carrying two steaming cups of coffee.

"Wake up there, feller!" Ray chuckled, walking across the room.

Norman's eyes popped open. Readjusting in his chair, he stretched as Ray put the cup on the table by the bed. "I thought you might be a little tired after working all night, so I brought you a cup of joe."

"Thanks, Hollywood!" Norman yawned, "That'll come in handy."

"Hollywood? How did I earn that name?"

"You got your name in the Springfield paper, big boy! None of the rest of us were interviewed for that article about the fire."

Ray turned red and he looked down at the floor.

"Yeah," he said, still looking down. "Not sure how they got my name. Or even heard about it. But I guess that's a big city paper for you."

"Well I thought you did a nice job of it." Norman winked, then sipped his coffee. "Man, that does the trick. Thanks, brother, I needed that."

"Knew you would, bud."

Norman paused for a moment, looking at the floor.

"What's on your mind there, feller?" Ray noticed Norman looking at the floor.

"Ray, you said in that article that you thought it was the wood stove or the old kerosene heater that started the fire. Do you really think so?"

"Well, that was the first thing that popped into my head as to why the place would go up like that. That flue didn't get cleaned very often, you know, and I'm sure they had the old cast iron stove running hot that night. You remember how sometimes things would get so hot, we'd look up and see Mom's wallpaper on the ceiling burning away from the ole chimney. That was one hot fire to do that. Could've been that hot of a fire goin'. Who knows, they might have thrown a stick of hedge in there. I figure either that, or that kerosene heater got dragged out and set up and it was too close to something. So that's my best guess. Do you have a different idea?"

Norman took another sip of coffee.

"Well, personally, I think it might have been electrical." Norman sat up in his chair, turning to look at Ray. "Let me explain: Based on what we've been told, when Neil saw the place was on fire, he woke everyone up. So he, Mom, and Dad jumped out that north window. At the same time those three are jumping, including Dad hanging around too long in the bedroom to put on his overalls,

Dewey, Virginia, and little Gary are in the other room. Dewey's trying to get Virginia to jump, but she's scared. She finally jumps and then the floor caves in under Dewey. It all happens at about the same time. If Dad lingered in the north bedroom as long as Dewey stood in the south bedroom, and the floor collapsed under Dewey, who didn't weigh anything but didn't collapse under Dad, who weighs a lot more than Dewey, that tells me that the fire was more intense in the kitchen than the living room. So it couldn't have been the old wood stove."

"Think about this," Norman continued. "Remember over by the south wall of the kitchen, all that stuff that was normally plugged into that one wall socket? They had the fridge, Mom's washing machine, and the coffee pot all plugged into that one spot. If one of those, especially that old coffee pot, developed a short, it would have caused that kitchen to go up like a matchstick. That's why I think it was electrical."

Ray looked at the floor and thought about it for several seconds then looked at Norman.

"Yeah, I can understand your thinking. You may be right. Shame we'll never know for sure."

"Yeah." Norman took another sip of coffee then leaned back in his chair and looked at the ceiling as Ray watched Sarah sleep. Neither man said anything for several minutes.

"That's awful good coffee, Ray."

"Yep."

12:10 p.m.
St. John's Hospital, Room 425

Down the hall from Sarah, Orville's brother-in-law Glen "Pete" Franklin stepped into the room and gasped.

My God, can that be him? It doesn't even look like Orville.

Lying in the stark, cold room with an IV in his arm and an oxygen tube in his nose, Orville lay unconscious covered with only a sheet. His face, no longer black from the soot of the fire, was swollen to the point that he was nearly unrecognizable and colored an unpleasant mix of red splotches from his burns and yellowish gray from the lack of oxygen he had suffered from all the smoke he inhaled. The morphine which was regularly injected into his IV tube kept him unconscious while the pneumonia continued to consume his lungs and reduce his ability to breathe.

Glen stepped further into the room, followed by Jack Ritter, the son of Orville's brother Dick. The room, stark and unwelcoming with its simple white tiled walls and brilliant white light overhead, maintained a low air temperature. The large window in the room could have ushered in warm sunlight, but the curtains were drawn. Heavy wooden armchairs on either side of the bed, the only indications that anyone was welcome in the room, awaited the two men.

A nurse, checking his IV, oxygen tube, and the overall condition of his arms, turned when she heard footsteps.

"Are you gentlemen family?" the young nurse inquired.

"Yes, I'm his brother-in-law, Glen Franklin. Everyone calls me Pete," Glen answered then pointed at Jack. "Jack here is Orville's nephew."

"Nice to meet both of you, I'm Susan, and I'm his nurse for this afternoon" nodded the nurse. "If you gentlemen are going to be here for a while, please keep an eye on his arms. He has a tendency to swing his arms about. He started having seizures this morning, which is typical for the damage to the brain and his condition with the pneumonia. Just please keep him from further hurting himself when he flings his arms about."

"Yes, ma'am, will do. Can we open the curtains to let some sunlight in?" Glen moved toward the window.

"No, I'm sorry, that's not good for him. His eyes are damaged from the fire, and the burns on his skin will hurt worse if direct sunlight hits them. The curtains must stay closed," Susan directed before walking out the door.

"Let's stand on either side of him, Jack," Glen directed, pointing to the nearest side of the bed. "You take that side, I'll go over to the other side."

Leaning over the rails on either side of the bed, each man instinctively grabbed one of Orville's hands and squeezed.

"Uncle Orville?" Jack asked quietly.

"You're probably going to have to speak louder, son." Glen nodded toward Orville. "He's sedated. We may not know if he can hear us."

"Uncle Orville, it's Jack." Jack squeezed Orville's hand as he spoke louder. “Pete and me, we are here with you. It’s going to be okay.”

“Hey brother.” Glen leaned in close. “We’re here for you buddy. It’s going to be alright, Orv. You just lay there and get better. We’re here.”

Without opening his eyes, Orville let out a weak quiet moan.

Jack looked at Orville then at Glen.

“Do you think he heard us? Does he know we’re here?”

“No way of knowin’.” Glen shook his head. “We just have to try, just in case. Not a bunch of talk. Just say something to him ever’ once in a while.”

Both men lowered their heads and stood quietly, still holding on to Orville’s hands.

After several minutes of shallow breathing, Orville let out a long, weak cough. Jack and Glen looked up as he strained to clear his lungs, and shifted in his bed, unconsciously wincing from the pain.

“Shiiiit,” Orville uttered weakly, his voice hoarse and gravelly.

Jack made eye contact with Glen, and Glen winked.

“At least his vocabulary hasn’t changed any,” Glen joked.

“Uncle Orville.” Jack leaned in, speaking loudly again. “I thought you might like to know I sold that old Chevy you always complained about. Some old fool gave me exactly what I was asking for it.”

Orville let out a weak moan.

Jack looked at Glen again.

“Pete?”

“He might hear you.” Glen nodded.

“Uncle Orville, Norma Rea said to tell you hi and she loves you.”

No response. Just shallow breathing.

Jack looked back at Glen.

“It’s okay, son. Chances are we won’t know for sure if he hears us.”

The two men quieted again, content to stand with Orville and listen to him breathe.

After several minutes of silence, Orville frowned hard, his teeth grinding as his jaws clinched. His arms lifted off the bed and flailed about. Alarmed, Jack and Glen grabbed Orville’s arms quickly.

“He’s having one of those seizures! He’s going to hurt himself or pull that IV out,” Glen yelled, grabbing Orville’s right arm. “Jack, grab his arm and hold it down."

Both men leaned in and put their weight on Orville's arms as he continued to thrash about. A low gurgling growl came from deep in his chest.

Suddenly Orville's hands clenched tightly in a fist, and both men felt his arms tense. As they stood on either side of him, holding his arms down, Orville flexed and tried to raise his arms.

"Man, he's strong," Glen whispered, watching Orville's face, twisted and angry.

"Hard to hold down!" Jack grunted.

Orville's seizure continued while both men struggled to hold his arms.

Orville let out another low growl and lifted Jack and Glen off the floor. Both men quickly grabbed the rails on both sides of the bed to steady themselves as they continued to hold on to Orville.

"Pete!" Jack whispered as he rose.

"Orv…" Glen called out loudly to his brother, "Orv, it's okay… Orv, you're safe."

After a few seconds, Orville slowly relaxed his arms and let Jack and Glen back down, his jaws relaxed and the frown disappeared. He drifted away again, back to sedation.

"Pete! He lifted us off the ground!" Jack's eyes were huge.

"He's always been a strong little fart." Glen winked. "It's okay, son. But I need to step outside and tell the nurses what just happened. Keep an eye on him and I'll be right back."

As Glen left the room, Jack grabbed Orville's hand again and gave it a gentle squeeze.

"I sure hope you can hear me, Uncle Orville. You just lay there and get better, okay? Hang in there, uncle."

12:10 p.m.
St. John's Hospital, Room 420

In Neil's room, nothing broke the silence.

The curtains, barely cracked open, allowed in just enough light to see around the stark room, adding to the gloom within.

Neil, sitting up in his bed with his knees pulled up close to him, stared off into the distance, through the wall across from him. Every few minutes he reached up to feel the gash on his forehead, now healing, thanks to a couple of stitches administered in the emergency room when he first arrived at the hospital. The bandage was off, so he would run his fingers across the wound, feeling the stitches and slight bump, then look down and shake his head, then drift off again to whatever he saw beyond the wall across from him.

His sister Margaret sat quietly next to the bed, watching him. When Neil and the twins were small, Sarah required the three girls to help watch over and take care of the boys. With nine children and a household to take care of, Sarah needed help, and called on the girls to lend a hand. June was assigned to Delbert, Wanda to Delmas, and Margaret to Neil. Now on her own and engaged to be married, Margaret hadn't needed to take care of Neil for several years but now felt needed again, and sat watching.

Poor dear. I don't know what to say to him right now. He's not even here. I think he's back to that night. Whatever he saw and heard, he's still there.

"Neil, honey," she finally spoke up, "do you need anything?"

Neil shook his head without looking at her.

"Do you want to talk?" She knew the answer ahead of time.

Again, Neil only shook his head.

"Well, that's okay. I'm going to be right here, little brother, if you need anything."

Breaking his stare, Neil glanced toward Margaret. He stretched out his left arm and opened his hand. Understanding, Margaret scooted her chair closer to the bed and leaned over and grasped his hand, as Neil closed his fingers tightly around hers.

He turned and looked at her. She noticed a tear running down his face. Her eyes welled up as she cracked a pained smile at him. He smiled weakly back.

12:10 p.m.
St. John's Hospital, Room 412

Virginia's room was filled with sunlight and flowers in an attempt to keep her spirits up. Jerry, Norman's wife, sat next to Virginia's bed, as the two women visited quietly.

"Jerry, have you seen Neil?" Virginia inquired.

"Yes. Only for a few minutes. His sisters have seen him more than I have." Jerry looked down.

"Is he doing okay?"

"He's taking it very hard. He has the least injuries, at least on the outside. But he's sure hurting on the inside."

"Bless his heart… he… you know he…" Virginia stopped as her abdomen tensed for a moment then relaxed. "I shouldn't say this…"

"What, honey?" Jerry turned to look at Virginia.

"He screamed a lot in the ambulance. Not like hollering out in pain. He screamed."

Virginia turned away from gazing at the ceiling and looked at Jerry.

"They put Neil and me together in the lead ambulance. He laid there, next to me, screaming about Dewey. Sometimes he screamed so loud and so much, I could hardly hear the siren." Virginia grinned weakly as she wiped the tear that escaped her eye and rolled down her cheek.

Jerry reached over and grasped Virginia's hand.

"That must have been a tough ride, sweetie." Jerry winked.

Virginia turned and began staring at the ceiling again. Jerry sat back in her chair and watched her.

Something else is on her mind. I'm just going to wait till it comes out.

The room was silent for only a short time.

"I have something awful I need to say, Jerry, but at the same time, I don't want to say it." Virginia frowned.

"Well, honey, you should go ahead and say it. Get it out," Jerry reassured, leaning over again and patting Virginia's hand.

"Well…" Virginia held her breath as she held her thought.

"It's okay, dear, let it out This will just be between you and me."

"Jerry… I hate to say it… but…" Virginia shook her head. "I… I didn't want to stay at that house that night. I… I had… bad feelings about it."

"What kind of feelings, Virginia?"

Virginia turned and looked at Jerry, still scowling.

"Well… you know… there was the fact that they had no running water in that place."

Jerry smiled.

"Yeah, that's kind of a big deal, especially with a little one."

"Yeah." Virginia shook her head. "I just couldn't see staying several days in that house. But I knew Dewey wanted to, and they needed to have some time with him and Gary."

"And you, too, dear! You meant the world to them. I mean, you mean the world to them, honey! They wanted to see you too." Jerry shifted in her chair.

"I think you had it right the first time." Virginia's eyes welled up with tears. "I *meant* something to them. Not now. They don't love me now."

Jerry reached over and grabbed Virginia's hand.

"Now, Virginia, you know that's not true! Everyone loves you! You're family!"

"I'm not anymore! My Dewey and Gary, they are both gone! And it's my fault!"

Virginia began to sob.

"Now, honey…" Jerry tried to reassure her.

"No, it's true!" Virginia interrupted, crying. "It's my fault! I was scared, Jerry! If I hadn't… If I had only jumped sooner, Dewey wouldn't have had to stand there so long… in the flames… there were flames everywhere, Jerry. We were all burning. My gown was smoking. The lace even melted, melted into my chest! One more second, and I would have been on fire myself. Gary was screaming so loud, and then Dewey pushed me. It was my fault, Jerry! How could they love me now? I'm not even a Ritter now…"

Jerry squeezed Virginia's hand tightly.

"Virginia! Listen to me!"

Virginia refused to look at Jerry, turning toward the wall.

"Virginia. Look at me, honey."

Virginia turned back to look at Jerry. Both women had tears running down their faces.

"Virginia, this family loves you. Ritters love deeply and they don't let go of anyone. No one blames you for what happened. We all would have been scared, too. Honey, the fire was too hot below you guys. The floor couldn't hold up. Just a few more seconds and all three of you would have died."

"But at least we would have all died together!" Virginia blurted out, sobbing.

"Oh, honey, no. You survived for a reason. You're still here to carry on their memory. We love you. You will always be a part of this family."

"I wish I could believe that, I really do." Virginia looked back to the wall. “But I don’t want to be here without them. I’m so ashamed… So ashamed that I lived. I wish I would have died with them.”

Jerry quietly hung her head.

Dear God, she means it.

13

October 31, 2:28a.m.
St. John's Hospital, Room 420

Neil stirred.

His closed eyes detected a change in light. Something somewhere was brighter.

A quick blink.

Orange.

Another quick blink.

Orange.

He rolled over and went back to sleep.

2:29a.m.

Neil stirred again.

Through his closed eyes, he could tell the room was still brighter.

"Too early for chow," he mumbled as he ran his fingers through his hair.

His eyes still closed, Neil shifted in his bed. Propping up on his right elbow, he leaned right, barely opened his eyes, and blinked hard twice, looking at the wall to his right.

Orange.

He sighed then laid back down.

"Who… who turned on a light?" he muttered.

Another long sigh, he propped up onto his left elbow, leaned left and squinted.

Bright orange.

He blinked hard again, struggling to open his eyes.

Then he saw… it…

He shrieked.

There, beside his bed, stood a blackened, nearly skeletal Dewey, completely engulfed in flames.

"Dewey!"

"You know you coulda gotten to me, Neil," Dewey spoke from within the flames.

"But... but… I tried, Dewey," Neil stammered, his terrified bloodshot eyes wet with tears.

"Aw bullshit. You shoulda come burn with me."

"No, Dewey, I tried but that beam came down and…"

"Cut the crap, Neil. You coulda burned, too. Come on."

Dewey stretched out a burning arm.

"Come burn with me!" Dewey lurched forward and grabbed Neil's hand. Neil screamed, Dewey's flames burning into his skin.

"Come on, Neil! Burn with me!" Dewey laughed as he pulled Neil out of bed with one hard yank and sent him flying toward the wall next to him.

Neil hit the wall and went through it, landing in a pile of burning lumber from the farmhouse. Dewey popped his blackened head up through the cinders.

"See? You coulda done this if you'd just tried harder, you little shit!" Dewey growled, "Duck!"

Just then, Orville, engulfed in flames, fell through the ceiling and landed on Neil, knocking him deeper into the burning cinders.

Screaming, Neil pushed Orville off, grabbed a concrete block next to him, and pulled himself up out of the cinders into the flaming kitchen of the old farmhouse as Dewey grabbed his shirt and held on.

"Come on back in here Neil!" Dewey barked as Neil tried to pull his shirt away from Dewey's burning hands.

Just then, that same flaming wooden beam from the kitchen came down and hit Neil in the head. Rolling back, he looked down and saw a large shard of window glass stuck in his arm. He screamed as he pulled the glass out of his arm. Tossing it aside, Neil looked around for Dewey.

"Dewey? Where are you?"

"I'm out here! Neil, help me! Neil!"

Dewey's voice was coming from the hall. Neil ran out the door.

"Dewey?"

"Here I am!"

Neil looked left and saw Dewey, still engulfed in flames, dart around the corner of the hallway, its walls blackened from the fire as he ran by. Neil took off after him.

"You coulda saved me!" Dewey yelled from the next hallway.

Neil rounded the corner, yelling, "I tried, Dewey! I tried!"

At the next corner, the wooden floor burst into flames in front of Neil and collapsed. Raising his arms to protect himself from the flames, Neil looked in time to see Dewey falling through the flames. Down, down, down further he went. Through the floor below, then the next, then the next…

"Dewey! Dewey!"

"Mr. Ritter! Mr. Ritter! Please wake up! You're having a bad dream! Mr. Ritter!"

Neil looked around wildly.

"Where's Dewey?"

"Mr. Ritter, Dewey isn't here. I'm sorry but he's not here." The nurse gently held his shoulders, keeping him steady.

"Where am I?" Neil's wide eyes began to focus as he looked at each of the six nurses around him, sweat running down the side of his face.

"Mr. Ritter, you're at the hospital. This is the fourth floor. You're safe, Mr. Ritter."

"No, but Dewey! He… he fell through the floor! He fell through this floor. I saw him! He… he… was on fire…" Panting, Neil looked down at his bandaged feet and his white hospital gown then noticed the blood dripping down his left arm. He looked at the nurses again, as one of them put a bandage around his arm.

"Where's…. where's Mom?" Neil turned his head and looked down the hall.

"Your mom is down the hall sleeping. We are taking good care of her, I promise."

"What about Dad?"

"He's just down the hall, too."

"Wha… but… Virginia?"

"She's sleeping down the hall. She's okay."

Neil looked down at the floor, suddenly realizing he was in the middle of the hall.

"I tried to save him." Tears began to trail down Neil's cheeks. "Really I tried to save him! But the beam! And it was hot! Too hot to get to him! I tried!" Neil clenched his fists as he pleaded with the nurse.

"Come on, Mr. Ritter. Let's get you back to your bed." The nurse gently turned Neil around to the door of his room. As she guided him in, she quietly turned to another nurse and mouthed "sedative" to her.

"You must have torn out your IV when you jumped up out of bed," she said softly, helping Neil settle down into his bed. "We're going to get another one started, and we will give you a little something special to help you rest."

"But… the glass… that big piece of glass from the window… it was in my arm. And the flames. I was in the flames with Dewey!"

She gently rested her hand on the left side of his face and smiled as he looked up at her.

"It's going to be okay, Mr. Ritter. You're safe here. We're going to take good care of you. Just relax."

Neil began to calm down as the nurse administered a sedative into his new IV. Just as his eyes grew heavy, he looked down at his left arm and noticed the black marks on his wrist, from where Dewey's flaming hand grabbed him.

14

October 31, 11:40 a.m.
St. John's Hospital, Room 425

The room, crowded beyond capacity, was silent. No one spoke. Fourteen people stood in the small dark room, far exceeding the hospital's standard allowance. Understanding the situation, the nursing staff bent the rules that morning, and turned a blind eye to the overcrowded situation.

Barely clinging to life, Orville laid unconscious before his family, his shallow breaths almost undetectable. In the preceding days as the pneumonia consumed his lungs, his skin took on an ashen gray color, at least in the areas not red or black from his burns. Now, near death, he lay nearly unrecognizable.

No one sat during the vigil. Norman and Jerry stood holding hands next to Wanda and Speedy on the far side of the bed, while Ray and Barbara stood next to Delbert and Dorothy on the side nearest the door. Margaret, Boyd, Delmas, Mary, June and her husband Jim made a semicircle at the foot of the bed, June and Margaret each resting a hand on one of Orville's feet.

Norman broke the exhausting silence.

"It won't be long now, folks. I think we need to say whatever we're going to while he's still alive. Jerry, you start, I'll go last."

Jerry took in a deep breath, wiping her eyes with a tissue.

"Thank you, Papa, for making me feel like your daughter." She turned to Wanda as she began to cry harder. "I… I think that's all I can… get out..."

"I… I… can't…" Wanda sobbed.

"Don't you worry none, Orv." Speedy nodded, "Thanks for everything, ole buddy."

Speedy started to step back away from the bed, but Wanda grabbed his hand and pulled him close.

"Oh, Daddy." June sniffed, trying to hold back tears. "I'm going to miss you. I wish you could stay. I wish… I wish… I love you, Daddy."

"Till we meet again, my friend." Jim cleared his throat, his head bowed.

"I wish we could have met," Mary said softly, squeezing his foot. "Rest well, Mr. Ritter."

Delmas cleared his throat.

"I, uh," he stammered, "wish you… didn't have to go, Dad. That's all."

Delbert didn't look up. "Love you, Dad."

"I'm sure going to miss you, Daddy." Margaret wiped her eyes as she spoke. "Gonna miss you a lot."

"Orv…" Boyd stumbled with his words. "Orv, you rest now. Just rest."

Dorothy cleared her throat, tears streaming down her face.

"Mr. Ritter, I, uh… I hope somehow you can see all of us gathered here. I hope you know how much we all love you. We… we're all going to be okay. You can go now and rest. We… we bid you a safe journey to the other side." Dorothy lowered her head as Delbert squeezed her hand.

Barbara, standing next to Dorothy, took her right hand and gave it a squeeze.

"I'm not so sure I can top that." She grinned as she squeezed Dorothy's hand.

Everyone snickered, easing the pain of the moment.

"You're a good man, Orville Ritter," Barbara blurted out, "a damn good man. See you again someday."

"You, uh," Ray stammered, "you tell the grandparents hi for us when you get up there, Dad."

Ray looked up at Norman, as tears welled up in both men's eyes.

"Your turn, big brother." Ray nodded.

"Don't you worry 'bout a thing, Dad," Norman started, his voice booming in the small room, "We're going to take good care of Mom, Neil, and Virginia…" He paused for a moment. "Tell Dewey hi for us." Another pause. "We're going to miss…"

Before Norman could get out "you," Orville took in a noticeable breath, then exhaled. His head tilted to the right, toward Norman, then all was silent.

No one moved for several seconds. The only sound in the room was an occasional sniff. Then almost simultaneously, each couple turned in to each other and cried quietly.

After a few moments, Norman pulled away from Jerry.

"I need to let them know out there that he's gone."

"I… I know, love," Jerry was still crying.

Wanda turned and held an arm out to Jerry and pulled her in as Speedy wrapped his big arm around her and held both women.

Norman left the room and stepped quickly down the hallway to the nurses' station.

"Ma'am," he said to the first nurse he encountered, "Just wanted to let you know Mr. Ritter in 425 just passed."

The other nurses at the station stopped their conversation and turned to look. Norman glanced briefly at them, then back.

"Oh, Mr. Ritter, I'm so sorry. I'll call for Doctor Lockhart. He's here somewhere making his rounds. I'll make sure he gets there quickly."

"Thank you, ma'am." Norman nodded and started to turn to walk back down the hall.

"Oh, Mr. Ritter?"

"Yes, ma'am?" Norman stopped and turned.

"Is the rest of the family still in there with him?"

"Yes, ma'am."

"Okay. Take all the time you need." The nurse smiled and nodded.

Norman nodded in appreciation then turned and walked back to the room.

"I need to go get Neil," Wanda said, pulling away from Speedy and Jerry, "He's going to want to see Daddy one last time."

She stepped quickly out of the room as everyone began to pull apart from their hugs and compose themselves. Delmas, Delbert, and Ray pulled their handkerchiefs out of their pockets and blew their noses at the same time, eyeballing each other as they did it.

Norman stepped back in the room and looked around.

"Where's Wanda?"

"She took off to bring Neil in," Speedy spoke up.

Norman raised his eyebrows and nodded.

Room 420

Neil's room, located across the hall and five doors down from Orville's, required a short walk for Wanda, but felt like an eternity.

What am I going to say? How do I tell him Daddy's gone? How is he going to react? He seems so on edge. I'm worried about him. I should have asked Speedy to come with me.

The door to Neil's room was only slightly ajar, and no lights were on. Wanda knocked softly on the door as she slowly pushed it open.

"Neil? You awake, little brother?" she whispered, stepping timidly into the room.

"Hi, sis." Neil turned to see Wanda walking in.

"How you doing, buddy?" Wanda asked, leaning over to kiss his cheek. As she pulled away, she noticed the bandage on his forehead was gone, showing the large gash in his forehead. "Looks like your forehead is starting to heal."

"Yeah, they took the bandage off this morning. Guess I'm doing okay," Neil cracked a weak smile. "How's everyone doing?"

Wanda pulled a chair over beside Neil's bed and sat down.

"Well, Mom is still unconscious most of the time. They are keeping her heavily sedated. Her burns are really bad and they said they want to keep her knocked out to keep her from being in much pain."

Neil nodded.

"Virginia is healing up okay. With that broken pelvis, she's pretty much confined to her bed. But the doctor is apparently optimistic and says she may get to go home in a couple of weeks if her healing continues like it is."

"That's real good," Neil said numbly. "How's Dad?"

"Well…" Wanda shifted in her chair. "Uh, Neil, Daddy's… uh…"

A tear ran down her face. Neil looked at her.

"He's gone, Neil."

Neil's eyes welled up with tears.

"When?"

"Just a couple of minutes ago."

"Did he ever wake up?"

"No. All of us were in there. He just took one last breath and went."

Neil looked down, tears streaming down his face.

"Neil, honey, he's still in the room, if you'd like to go see him. I can take you."

Neil took a deep breath.

"No… I don't think so. I don't want to see him like that. I want to remember him alive… not dead. Thank you though, sis. Thanks for checking on me."

"Alright, little brother." Wanda got up. "If you're sure. It would be no trouble to walk you over there, you know."

Neil looked up and smiled weakly again.

"I know. Thank you, sis."

Wanda blew him a kiss and slipped back out of the room. After she left, Neil rolled over slowly in his bed and looked out the window.

"Bye, Dad," he whispered, crying, "I'm so sorry. Sorry I didn't wake up sooner. Oh Dad, I'm so sorry."

Room 425

Everyone except Norman had cleared out of Orville's room by the time Wanda walked back in. Norman stood at the foot of the bed with his hands on the rails, lost in his own thoughts, speaking quietly while looking at his lifeless father.

"Dad, you always told me that someday I would be in charge of the family. I didn't know I'd be this age when it happened. I'll take good care of everyone. I'll make you proud. I've always wanted to make you proud of me." He ducked his head.

"He was proud of you, big brother." Wanda had walked up closely without Norman noticing. She slipped her arm around him.

"He's always been proud of you."

Norman turned and wrapped his arms around his sister and held on tight. Wanda held him as she felt his body quiver, realizing he was finally crying.

"Let it out, Norman," she whispered, "You don't always have to be the rock, you know."

After several seconds, Norman regained his composure and pulled away from Wanda.

"Thanks, sis." Norman smiled as Wanda reached up and wiped the tears from his face. "Guess I need to call Clinkingbeard and the rest of Ava to let them know. Is Neil coming?"

"No, he said he didn't want to see Dad like this. He wants to remember him like before."

"Well, okay then," Norman shook his head. "We all handle it in different ways, I guess."

"His bandage is gone now, the one on his forehead. It's a terrible looking gash. He's got a little bruise there, too."

"Sounds like he's healing up pretty well though, right?" Norman asked.

"Yes, on the outside at least." Wanda looked down. "But I worry about him, Norman. You know, Dewey was screaming for him to come help him. He remembers all that. I'm afraid he's hurting really badly inside."

"It'll be alright, sis. He may have to toughen up a bit to get through it."

Just then, Dr. Lockhart knocked on the door and stepped in slowly, followed by two orderlies. Nodding and smiling at Norman and Wanda, he walked over and looked at Orville.

"I'm so sorry about this, folks. Wish he could have woke up at least to communicate at some point, but I think it's just as well in the long run. He would have been in terrible pain."

"Yes. Yes, I guess it's better that he didn't feel anything," Wanda brought a tissue up to her nose.

"At least that we know of," Norman said blankly, staring at Orville. "Doctor Lockhart, if I may ask, what do you plan to put down as his cause of death?"

"Well, bronchial pneumonia is the main reason," Dr. Lockhart said, flipping through his notes. "But I would have to add the burns as a contributing factor. He's been burned very badly from lingering in the house. Although I must admit, Mrs. Ritter is burned far worse, even though from what I understand she jumped before Orville. I still can't get my head wrapped around that."

"Doctor," Wanda spoke up, "according to Neil, Mom ran around the back of the house while Neil ran around the front, when they heard Dewey screaming. It sounds like she tried to crawl back into the house to get to Dewey."

"Jesus." Doctor Lockhart shook his head. "That would explain it. She must be some kind of lady."

"She sure is, Doc." Norman smiled.

"Well, I hate to say it, but there's some paperwork to fill out." Lockhart shuffled through his papers again. "Mr. Ritter, do you feel up to doing this, before time gets away from us?"

"Sure." Norman smiled. "Let's get it done."

"Well, if you'll pardon me," Wanda interrupted, "I'm going to slip out and rejoin the others in the waiting room."

"Okay, sis." Norman winked as Wanda turned and walked out, closing the door behind her.

15

November 2, 1959
Clinkingbeard Funeral Home, Ava, Missouri

In the aftermath of the fire, the family originally planned to bury Dewey and Gary together on Friday, October 30th. However, when Orville's death appeared imminent, Norman contacted Clarence Clinkingbeard to delay the funeral so that the three could be buried at the same time. Holding all three services at once seemed to make sense, and in some small way eased the burden a little, to prevent everyone from having to go through the funeral process multiple times. No one in the family, though, realized how much of a shock the entire city of Ava felt, especially over the loss of a young father and son. Aside from collection jars and the vote from the Good Neighbor Club, a pie supper took place Thursday night to benefit the family. Complete with musical entertainment, the event was held at Star Chapel five miles east of Ava, offering the community an opportunity to do what they could to lend a hand. Upon hearing of the death of Orville, now the third victim of the fire, the entire town grieved, preparing itself for a triple funeral to be held on Monday, November 2 at 2:00 p.m.

Only two caskets were required for the sad event. Since Gary was just a toddler, the family agreed that his remains should be buried with those of Dewey. Everyone felt that father and son should be together. Both caskets remained closed at all times.

Two funeral books were maintained, one for Dewey and Gary, one for Orville. In each book, over 300 signatures filled the pages, and the recorder of the flowers received had to stop entering information at 92 arrangements. There simply wasn't any room left in the books for additional flower arrangement information.

The family recruited Reverend William Spindler to perform the service. Spindler, well acquainted with the Ritters, performed several family weddings and funerals throughout the years. Upon hearing of the tragedy, he called regularly on Neil and Virginia, and checked in on Sarah and Orville in their sedated conditions, while all of them were being treated at St. John's.

By 1:15 p.m. on November 2, the parking lot at Clinkingbeard's Funeral Home was full, and the grieving population of Ava began to park one block away on the school grounds. Sheriff Souder coordinated with the Ava Police Department to assist with traffic control, with patrol cars at either end of Spring Street and Mansfield Road to keep things from getting out of hand. The officers knew they were going to be needed afterwards when all those cars made their way north to Ava Cemetery for the graveside service. Once he felt like everything was under control, Don joined his wife Stella and stepped into the chapel, receiving hugs and handshakes from the entire family. After greeting everyone, the Souders took a seat next to Dick Ritter and his family.

The inflow of relatives and friends continued nonstop well past the planned 2:00 start time. Knowing in advance that this funeral could be the largest in his company's history, Clarence Clinkingbeard did not schedule anyone in his second, smaller chapel, and left it open for the potential overflow crowd. By the time Reverend Spindler started the funeral service, the overflow chapel, the outer hall, and the main chapel exceeded their capacities.

Just before walking to the front of the chapel to bring things to order, Reverend Spindler grabbed Clarence by the arm.

"This is going to be a tough one, Clarence." Spindler sighed.

"Yeah, Bill, it is. This whole thing has upset me more than I've been in a long time. But guys like you and I must be strong for the family, mustn't we?"

"Yes indeed, we must. Thanks, Clarence. Here we go." Spindler patted Clarence on the shoulder and walked to the podium at the front of the main chapel, as the room, then the hallway then the second chapel quieted to a hush.

None of Reverend Spindler's words of comfort were recorded in the funeral books. He no doubt spoke of the tragedy as well as the shock borne by not only the family but also the community. Four singers and an organist were present, organized by Orville's sister Dora Franklin. Don Souder squeezed Stella's hand hard when the quartet began to sing "What a Friend We Have in Jesus."

"You're not going to believe this," Don whispered, leaning over to his wife as tears welled up in his eyes, "but the neighbors sang that song when they stood over the family that night. They sang that very song to keep their spirits up."

After conclusion of the service, rather than have everyone file by the closed caskets, Spindler dismissed everyone to their cars to meet at the Ava Cemetery for the graveside comments. Many people lingered, nonetheless, while six friends of the family serving as pallbearers slowly loaded the caskets into the hearses, the same vehicles which transported Virginia, Neil, and Sarah to the hospital in the early morning hours after the fire. While the caskets were loaded into the cars, George Pledger, recorded in the funeral book as an honorary pall bearer, stood by watching and holding back the tears.

The area around the burial plots, located side by side about halfway down the west hillside of the cemetery, easily accommodated the hundreds of attendees who covered the grounds all the way to the top. Spindler invited all who could to come as close as possible, in hopes that everyone could hear his final remarks. Some people, standing on the hillside listening to Spindler, began to whisper among themselves, wondering what was in the second casket. Was it empty? Did anyone ever find the remains of Dewey and Gary? Maybe they just put in ashes scooped from the site as representative remains. Many wondered what secrets the second casket might hold, but no one dared ask the family.

2:25 p.m.
St. John's Hospital, Room 401

"I know why you're here."

Virginia's sudden statement after a long period of silence startled

Neva Vinson and Lula Dye out of their perusal of magazines. The two women looked at each other and then at Virginia. Each assumed that Virginia would be unconscious most of the day, due to her pain medication.

"I know why you've come to sit with me today."

"We came because we wanted to see you, dear." Neva smiled as she reached out for Virginia's hand.

"Well, that may be true, and I certainly thank you for that, Miss Neva. But I know what today is." Tears welled up in Virginia's eyes and rolled down her face.

"It's Monday, dear!" Lula chimed in, leaning over to pat Virginia's bed.

"Yes, ma'am, it's Monday." Virginia turned and looked away as tears began to roll down her cheeks again. "It's Monday, November 2, and today they are burying my Dewey and Gary. And Papa Orv, too. And I can't be there. I… I can't get out of this bed…" She began to cry harder. "…to be there for the funeral of my own husband and son."

Both women sighed and quit smiling as Virginia began to sob.

"Yes, love, you are right." Neva leaned over and held Virginia's hand.

"Norman told me he had to make the arrangements with Clinkingbeard." Virginia turned back to Neva and her mother. "He said they are going to bury Dewey and Gary in the same casket."

"Yes, honey. You're right. Today is the day of the funeral. They are indeed burying Orville at the same time. And yes, Dewey and Gary are being buried in the same coffin."

Neva cleared her throat to choke back tears.

"I don't know if anyone told you both or not, but my Elga… he helped Mr. Clinkingbeard… he helped find them… in the house… I mean, the remains of the house… Oh, honey, I don't know how to properly say any of this. Poor Elga, he can't hardly sleep now. It's haunting him."

Virginia's eyes widened as Neva brought a tissue up to her nose.

"He said it's haunting him, Miss Neva?"

"Yes, dear. He can't get it out of his head, when they found them. He can't sleep. He said… he said… oh dear Jesus, I don't know if I should even say it." Neva looked down as she folded the tissue.

"Please… Miss Neva… What did Mr. Vinson say?"

Neva looked up and drew in a deep breath.

"He said… that they found… they found the bodies only a few feet apart. Under some rubble, about four feet from the edge of the house. He said he couldn't help but feel like Dewey held on… held on to the little guy as long as he could… while he fell." Tears rolled down Neva's face as she bit her bottom lip.

Unable to keep her composure, Virginia closed her eyes and began to sob loudly. Neva got up from her chair and leaned over to gently hold Virginia. All three women cried loudly together for several minutes.

Amidst the sobbing, Virginia cleared her throat.

"That's my Dewey. He was a good daddy. A good…" She took in a deep breath. "A good daddy to the end."

"Yes, love." Neva smiled as she brushed Virginia's hair away from her red, swollen eyes. "He was a good daddy."

"And a good husband," Virginia whispered then began to cry again. Neva held her until they were both exhausted from crying.

2:25 p.m.
Room 420

Down the hall from Virginia, Neil sat silently in his bed. His eyes, wide and bloodshot from crying and lack of sleep, stared blankly at a spot where the wall across from him met the ceiling. But his focus was not on that spot. His eyes were focused on something else, not in the room, something many miles away, and many nights ago. His forehead, still red from the burns suffered while trying to get to Dewey, showed signs of beginning to heal, his blisters receding.

To his right, LaVonne Kile, a pretty redhead, sat near the bed, also in silence, watching him stare.

He's not looking at the wall. He's looking past it, somewhere, to something. Where are you, handsome silent man?

LaVonne didn't actually know Neil very well. They met the previous summer through Ray's wife Barbara. On October 27th, in the evening edition, the Springfield newspaper ran a story on the fire, and upon reading the story, LaVonne recognized Neil's name as one of the hospitalized survivors. She decided she needed to call on him and just happened to pick November 2, the day of the funeral, to visit. She caught the bus near her house then walked two blocks from the bus stop to the hospital. She brought with her Juicy Fruit gum and a pack of cigarettes. Neil, polite and appreciative of the gum and cigarettes, sat silently while LaVonne tried to come up with things to say. Eventually she ran out of topics and just watched Neil stare, lost in his thoughts and grief.

After sitting in silence for what seemed like forever, LaVonne gathered her purse and stood up.

"I guess I should go, Neil. It was nice to see…"

Neil blinked and turned to look at her, gently grabbing her arm.

"No. Please don't go."

She looked at him and smiled. He wasn't smiling back, and she could see the pain in his eyes, the pleading to not be alone. She sat down again as he let go of her arm.

"You know," Neil said, clearing his throat, "if I had a penny, I'd give it to you."

He turned and smiled at LaVonne.

"Like a penny for my thoughts?" LaVonne smiled back.

Neil nodded, reaching out his hand for hers. She scooted her chair closer to the bed and reached over, resting her hand in his.

"Please stay," Neil whispered.

"Okay," LaVonne smiled.

16

November 12, 2:00 p.m.
St. John's Hospital

Dr. Lockhart called a meeting with family members to discuss Sarah's condition. Norman, Ray, Margaret, and Wanda huddled around the doctor in a corner of the waiting room on the fourth floor, down the hall from Sarah's room. Just a week prior, Neil, released from the hospital but still having nightmares, moved into Norman and Jerry's house, sleeping in an extra twin bed in their son Dennis' room. Then two days before the meeting, Virginia was released to convalesce at the home of her parents in Ava. Sarah, the only patient left from the fire, continued to slip in and out of consciousness.

"Folks, I called you here because I think we need to start waking your mom up a bit more." Dr. Lockhart began. "We've kept her heavily sedated because of the severity of her wounds. But we really can't keep that up much longer. She needs to start receiving special care for those burns, and we need to increase her caloric intake to help her heal. So I think it's best that we start weaning her off of the morphine and other pain medications. She needs to move, get up and walk around, and simply communicate."

No one spoke for a moment as Dr. Lockhart looked at all of them.

"Doctor," Norman spoke up, "I'm guessing this business of

waking her up is going to be touchy. I mean, as far as we all can tell, she doesn't even know that Dad is gone."

"You're exactly right, Norman. That's why I wanted to have this chat. When she wakes up and the fog starts to clear in her mind, she's going to have lots of questions. She won't realize initially how much time has passed. She will of course be upset about Mr. Ritter dying, especially since she didn't get to go to the funeral. She will want to know about Neil and Virginia, discovering that they have been discharged. And she will realize that she's the only member of the family still in the hospital. So we have to watch to make sure she doesn't get depressed. You will all have to rally around her to keep her spirits up. And all the while, she will be in pain because of the burns and the treatments we will be giving her."

"We can certainly do that." Ray jumped into the conversation. "All of us are taking turns, and will continue to do so."

"That's good. That's really good." Dr. Lockhart smiled and nodded at Ray. "Because that's what it's going to take. I would recommend that you all plan to keep a constant vigil over her. The nursing staff and I, we can take care of the medical end of things, but it's the personal side of this that will require the family. I suggest you even set up family members to spend the night. Sit up with her late into the night if she needs to talk or cry or whatever. I think that kind of effort will be absolutely necessary to get her through these next few months. At least until we see how she's going to handle everything."

"Our mother is a strong woman," Margaret said while playing with her hankie.

"Based on everything all of you have told me, I agree fully." Dr. Lockhart smiled. "And hopefully this period of constant vigil won't last long, and you all can keep working toward getting your lives back to something resembling normal. But for now, I think this is best."

"Well, Doc." Norman nodded. "We have to thank you for caring so much about our mother, and for paying attention to, you know, the human side of all of this. She's lucky to be in your care."

Dr. Lockhart stood up and shook Norman's hand while the rest of the group stood.

"Well, Norman, it's my pleasure." Dr. Lockhart smiled. "I'm looking forward to waking her up and getting to know her better."

Dr. Lockhart shook hands with everyone and bid them a good evening then left the room.

"Okay folks." Norman sighed. "Looks like we need to come up with a plan."

November 16, 10:45pm.
St. John's Hospital, Room 412

The soft glow of a table lamp threw shadows around the room while Mary and Dorothy sat in silence on either side of Sarah's bed. Thinking she was asleep, both ladies sat looking through magazines. Suddenly Sarah let out a large wet sniff, snapping them out of the articles they were reading. Lying flat on her back, she lay there, deep in the throes of a major cry. Instinctively, Mary and Dorothy tossed aside their magazines and each grabbed one of Sarah's hands.

Sarah turned and looked at each of them, squeezing each hand that held hers. Tears welled up in Mary and Dorothy's eyes, and they both got up and leaned over to gently hold on to her as she wept.

At one point, Sarah collected herself, and wiped her eyes with a tissue.

"I guess I need to toughen up and quit crying. People will start to think I'm just a big baby."

"Oh, honey," Dorothy spoke up, "you don't need to worry about what other people think. You've been through a lot, and we all know what's bothering you. It's better to get it out. We're here with you. Just get it out."

"Thank you, dear." Sarah sniffled, looking at Dorothy then Mary. "My boys are sure lucky to have you two."

Both Mary and Dorothy smiled.

"You know, girls, the reason I was crying so hard, I was just thinking about the night Orville and I first laid eyes on each other."

"Would it help if you told us about it?" Mary asked, still holding Sarah's hand.

Sarah let out a sigh. "Maybe so."

"I'd love to know how you met." Dorothy smiled, scooting closer to the bed.

Sarah let out another sigh and began to recollect.

"It was the Christmas evening service in 1920. I was three days

away from turning 19, and that night I was sitting next to mother in the rear pew of the Happy Home Church. Have either of you been to the Happy Home Church yet?"

Sarah looked at each girl. They shook their heads.

"It's a small wood-framed church on the northeastern outskirts of Ava, with a big iron potbelly stove in one corner."

She sniffed again and wiped her eyes with her tissue.

"As you can imagine, it was cold that night, so there was quite the fire roaring in that stove. Every time a log popped loudly in the stove, Dad would yell, 'Quiet, Satan!' which would get a big laugh. Anyway, while Daddy preached, I commenced to looking around the packed church, seeing who all was there. As I scanned the room, I caught the occasional glances of a handsome, dark-haired young man standing against the wall to my left. He had a firm square jaw and piercing green eyes, and he would quickly look away when he noticed me catching him staring. By the end of the service, he no longer looked away when our eyes met, and he cracked a tight smile more than once."

Sarah chuckled, remembering that night. Mary and Dorothy smiled at each other as they watched Sarah smile.

"After the service, I had to stand next to Mother and Daddy at the church doors, to greet everyone as they exited. That was expected of you when you were the preacher's daughter. I hated doing it, but I knew I would be in trouble later if I didn't do that, you know, and be on my best behavior. Daddy stood such that he greeted everyone first with his standard two-handed handshake. Have you ever seen Daddy shake hands?"

She looked at both girls, who again shook their heads.

"He has always had this certain way of shaking hands. Watch for it some time. He would shake hands with his right hand, of course, and at the same time cover the person's hand with his left. Mother stood next to Daddy in the role of the dedicated preacher's wife, making sure her courtesies were extended more to the ladies of the church than the men. I stood at the end, smiling pleasantly and shaking hands with everyone.

After almost everyone had filed out of the church and shaken hands with all three of us, that handsome young man appeared. Pulling on his tan wool coat as he slowly moved forward, he held a nice hat in front of him. He smiled and nodded and shook hands with

Daddy, quietly introducing himself. I thought he had a nice smile.

He sidestepped after shaking hands with Daddy and gently shook hands with Mother.

'Hello, son, I'm Lydia Seal, the parson's wife,' Mother said, smiling.

I heard him say, 'Hello, ma'am, I'm Orville Ritter. Very nice to make your acquaintance.'

His name stuck in my head.

'Orville Ritter,' Mother repeated, her eyes looking up as she thought out loud. 'You wouldn't be one of Simon and Liza Ritter's boys, would you?'

'Yes, ma'am,' Orville said, cracking a grin and looking down.

'I understand your grandmother Lee helped name this church,' Mother beamed, proud of herself for knowing so much about someone.

'Yes, ma'am, that's the story as I understand it.' Orville turned red and quickly glanced at me. I was already staring at him and smiling, which made him turn redder, and he looked down. I thought it was cute that I made him blush."

Sarah chuckled a little and grinned at Dorothy and Mary.

"Orville was Simon Ritter's second son, and he inherited his father's quiet nature. His older brother Bernie and younger brother Richard are taller than him by several inches and quite louder than him. Bernie and his wife Louise, along with Richard and Dora had made their way out of the church ahead of Orville, barely slowing down to exchange pleasantries with Daddy, Mother, and me.

'Awfully nice to make your acquaintance, Mrs. Seal.' Orville nodded and smiled, then sidestepped to me. I hadn't taken my eyes off of him during the conversation with Mother.

Orville's square jaw locked up as his steely green eyes met mine.

After a moment of silence, I reached out my hand, taking Orville's.

'Did I hear correctly that your name is Orville Ritter?' I couldn't help but smile as I felt his fingers wrap around my hand.

'Yes... yes, ma'am,' Orville stuttered, 'I'm, uh, Orville... Orville Ritter, ma'am, at, uh, at your service...'

'It is a pleasure to meet you, Mr. Ritter." I kinda cocked my head coyly and said, 'I trust you had a pleasant Christmas?'

'Oh yes, ma'am.' Orville nodded then looked down, having run

out of things to say.

I soooo wanted him to talk to me. Bless his heart, he was just so quiet.

'Pleasure to meet you, ma'am.' Orville nodded then stepped briskly away into the bright light of the evening's full moon, quickly putting on his hat.

I watched him walk away to join his brothers at the family's horse-drawn wagon. When he turned around to look back at me, he saw that I was still looking at him.

I kept thinking 'I want to talk with him again.'"

He continued to watch me as his brother Richard began to yell at their sister Dora, who was visiting with some girls her age. I noticed Orville's parents climbing into the wagon, and I assumed they were getting ready to leave. So I broke away from Mother and Daddy, who were busy visiting with the last people in line, and I walked quickly toward Orville, who was still standing alongside the wagon.

The bright full moon lit up the whole area. Richard, from his perch in the wagon, quit calling for Dora when he saw me coming toward Orville.

'Mr. Ritter,' I said, 'I meant to compliment you on your fine hat. I wouldn't want to miss praising such a wonderful appearance.'

Richard snickered from the wagon as he listened.

Orville quickly removed his hat and nodded, 'Thank you, Miss Sarah.'

I said, 'Mr. Ritter…'

'Please call me Orville, ma'am,' he said.

'Very well, Orville.' I couldn't help but grin. 'Do you have a long ride in the back of that wagon tonight to get home?' I was trying to come up with anything possible to say or ask.

'It's not too bad, ma'am…' he said.

'Call me Sarah,' I said.

Orville grinned.

'We live up over yonder.' Orville turned, pointing northwest. 'About a mile from here.'

'Well, it's a very cold night,' I said, reaching into the canvas bag that I used as a purse. I kept it tied to my wrist with a string. I brought out my hankie and handed it to him.

'Here, take this, please,' I said, 'in case you get the sniffles along the way.'

Looking down at the delicate hanky in his callused hand, Orville shook his head.

'Oh, Miss Sarah, I shouldn't,' he said. It was so cute. He said, 'You are very kind, but what if you catch a cold and do not have this delicate thing?'

'Don't worry about it,' I said, 'my mother has another one. Please take it, Orville. Consider it a Christmas present from me.'"

"Oh my gosh, that is sooooo romantic," Mary beamed.

Sarah let out a giggle. "It is, isn't it!" Sarah smiled, wiping a tear from her eye.

"Orville's face lost its grin and his eyes grew dark.

'I fear I have nothing to give you in return, Sarah,' he said.

I said, 'Christmas is about giving, Orville, and I am happy to give you my hanky as a present.'

He started to stutter and stammer, saying 'But... but... but.'

'Don't hurt my feelings by refusing my gift, Mr. Ritter,' I said, trying to look serious.

Orville quickly tucked the hanky in his pocket.

'Of course not, Sarah,' he said, 'I meant no offense.'"

"Awwwwwww," Dorothy beamed.

"'Very well,' I said, 'I see your parents are considering leaving.' I nodded toward Orville's parents, settling into the wagon seat. So I leaned in close and whispered, 'I wish you a Merry Christmas, Orville Ritter.'

He smiled again, his eyes flashing, and he said quietly, 'And a Merry Christmas to you, Sarah Seals.'

I turned and walked toward Mother and Daddy, who were still talking at the church door. When I got to where they were standing, I turned around again to watch Orville disappear into the darkness in the back of the wagon. Mother and Daddy finally finished their conversation and began to walk toward our wagon, with Mother in the lead as usual, saying goodbye to the lady she had been talking to. Daddy, looking toward Mother, stopped in front of me. I think I was still gazing into the darkness. Taking his pocketknife to cut a slab of twist tobacco he kept in his pocket, Daddy cleared his throat to get my attention.

'Nice young man, that Orville Ritter,' Daddy muttered then shoved the cut of tobacco into his mouth.

'Yes he is.' I think I sighed when I said it, but I wasn't really

paying attention to what Daddy really said.

Suddenly I realized what he was saying and I quickly turned and looked at him. He put his little knife back in his pants pocket then turned and looked at me, winked, and walked toward the wagon.

Two weeks later, Orville visited Daddy and asked his permission to call on me."

"Oh my! How did that go?" Dorothy blurted out.

"Not too bad, really," Sarah chuckled. "You know you always hear stories about the father of the girl being terrible to the boy calling on her. But based on what Daddy said at the church that night, it sounded like he thought favorably of Orville. So when he came to call on me, he and Daddy had a nice chat."

"Could you hear them talking?" Mary pressed for more information.

"Oh yes." Sarah nodded. "I was in the next room, trying to be quiet as a mouse while they talked. Orville was apparently sitting in the chair across the room from Daddy, who was sitting in his rocking chair, as usual.

"'Reverend Seals,' Orville started, 'I had the pleasure and privilege of meeting you, the lovely Mrs. Seals, and Miss Sarah at the Christmas Evening service at Happy Home Church.'

'Yes, I recall meeting you,' Daddy replied.

'Well, Reverend, uh... I came over today... uh... to respectfully ask your permission to call on Miss Sarah.'

Daddy didn't respond.

'I... I believe you may... uh... be familiar with my family and the kind of people we are,' Orville continued, still stammering a bit. 'I offer to be... uh... respectful at all times, and of course any calling on Sarah would be subject to your approval... and include all proper behavior.'

I heard Daddy stand up, and then Orville apparently stood up. I'm guessing they shook hands.

'Orville Ritter, you have my permission to call on Sarah,' Daddy said loudly. He knew I was in the next room listening.

'Thank you, sir,' I heard Orville say. I swore I could hear him smiling.

'This coming Sunday I will be preaching again at the Happy Home Church. Come to the service, and you may sit with Mrs. Seals and Sarah. You'll sit on the other side of my wife. After the church

service, you and Sarah are welcome to spend the afternoon together, under the supervision of myself and Mrs. Seals.'

'Thank you, sir,' Orville replied.

'You can come out now, Sarah,' Daddy called out, embarrassing me.

I stepped into the room and there stood Orville, shaking hands with Daddy. When he turned to look at me, still smiling, those eyes of his grabbed me and held on. I was so excited to see him.

'Good afternoon, Orville.' I nodded.

'Good afternoon, Miss Sarah.' Orville nodded back. 'I look forward to seeing you this Sunday.'

I said, 'I look forward to it as well.'

I glanced at Daddy and he was all smiles. I knew he approved.

That was January 1921 and in October of that same year we were married, with Daddy officiating."

Sarah wiped her eyes again.

"That's so sweet," Dorothy whispered, a single tear running down her face.

Sarah breathed in deep, letting it out slowly, staring at the wall across from her bed.

"I can't believe he's gone. The only man I've ever loved is gone. And I wasn't even conscious enough to know he was gone, let alone go to the funeral to pay my last respects. I just want to feel his arms around me again..."

Sarah couldn't say anymore. Tears rolled down her face and she began to weep loudly. Quickly wiping their eyes, Mary and Dorothy got up from their chairs at the same time and leaned over Sarah and gently held her, as all three ladies wept.

17

December 25, 1959, 7:00 p.m.
Norman Ritter's house, Springfield, Missouri

On Christmas evening, several of the siblings gathered at Norman's house. Despite the festive season, a gloom lingered over the family as everyone struggled to come to grips with their first Christmas without Orville, Dewey and Gary. Norman visited Sarah that afternoon, but by evening back at home he was exhausted, as the pressures of work added to the heavy burden of striving to hold the family together in the aftermath of the fire.

Neil continued to live at Norman's house, where the family laid witness to his occasional nightmares. Some nights they only heard grunts and moans coming from his bedroom. Other nights, they were awakened to him standing in the hallway screaming for Dewey. The entire household was rattled.

Norman, Ray, Speedy, Margaret's fiancé Boyd Parker, Delmas, and Delbert sat in the living room swapping stories and jokes while Jerry, Barbara, Wanda, Margaret, Mary, and Dorothy sat around the kitchen talking about kids, weddings, dinner, or anything else that kept them from talking about the fire or Sarah.

Neil, after spending most of the day in his room, came out to say hello to everyone. Looking a bit disheveled in his borrowed clothes, he said hello to everyone in the kitchen then walked into the living room where his brothers visited.

"Glad you could join us, Neil," Norman said, taking his cigarette from his mouth.

No one said a word. Neil pulled up a chair next to Norman's recliner and looked at the floor.

"Don't you think it's time you get a job, Neil?" Delmas asked.

Norman glared at him as Neil looked up.

"I'd like to," Neil answered quietly. "I'm… I'm having trouble sleeping still. Still having those nightmares. I just… I can't…"

"What the hell is the matter with you?" Delmas snapped, standing up and pointing at Neil. "Quit acting like a baby! You need to just drop it and go on, get on with your life!"

The other brothers turned toward Delmas, shocked by his outburst. The ladies in the kitchen immediately hushed to listen to the ruckus in the living room.

Neil turned red, his eyes welling up with tears.

"Little brother, you better cool it." Norman stood up, towering over Delmas. "I've heard him screaming. I've heard the nightmares. You haven't."

"It's okay, Norman," Neil uttered quietly behind Norman.

"No, it's not!" Norman snapped back. "Were you there, Delmas? Did you see what happened? Did you hear Dewey screaming?"

"No!" Delmas, still mad, glared at Norman.

"Then you get the hell off his back," Norman growled, poking his finger hard into Delmas' chest. "Neil will look for work after the first of the year."

Both men sat down again. No one said anything for several minutes. Then one by one, they began to talk again, as if the confrontation had not happened. But Norman kept an eye on Delmas the rest of the evening.

18

February 19, 1960 – 7:05 p.m.
St. John's Hospital, Room 412

The entire west wing of the fourth floor at the hospital buzzed with excitement. Sarah shifted nervously in her bed while nurses and aids darted in and out, repeatedly checking the room to make sure it was clean and orderly. Mildred Hodges giggled as she gave orders to everyone within hearing range.

"Do I look alright, Mildred?" Sarah looked in a little mirror and turned her head one way then the other, trying to get a good look at her hair. Earlier in the day, the hospital staff arranged for a lady from the in-house beauty shop to come to Sarah's room to wash and style her hair, and after being confined to the hospital for so long, Sarah gladly took her up on the offer, because tonight, in her room, a wedding was planned.

A couple of weeks earlier, while sitting in a booth drinking sodas at the café in Cranks department store, Delmas proposed to Mary. As she giggled and wiped her eyes with a tissue, she asked, "Where should we get married?"

"Well, I… I have a uh… special request, Mary," Delmas stammered. "Ya see, Mom has never gotten to see any of her kids get married up to this point. And uh… I suspect Maggie, Neil, and Delbert will get married soon, and she may still be in the hospital when that happens. So uh… what would you think about getting married in Mom's room at St. John's?"

Mary's eyes widened.

"Oh, Delmas, that's a wonderful idea," she beamed. "I love your mom, she's so sweet, so strong. I think that would be extra special for her. I'll tell Mom and Dad and will see if my brother Harry and his wife Barbara can make it. Harry has a camera, maybe he can take pictures."

"Sounds good to me. We will have to keep it small and simple since it's not a big room."

"Of course. Barbara can stand with me."

"And I'm sure Delbert will stand with me. I'll see if Norman and Neil can make it too."

He reached across the table and took her hand.

"Thank you, Mary. This is going to be great."

The entire hospital knew about the little ceremony, as news about St. John's first wedding spread throughout the building, and curious onlookers and well-wishers dropped by the room often.

"Honey, you look great," Mildred reassured.

"Do you think so? I swear this is the first time I've been this gussied up since I got here." Sarah chuckled briefly. "I want to look nice for the kids, and for Mary's family. I don't want to look bad. They're wealthy people, you know. I don't think they've ever been around simple farming types."

"Don't you worry about it, Miss Sarah. They will love you as much as we do."

"Thank you for the pretty new gown. Does it cover up my shoulder enough? Am I all covered up? I don't want them to see any of… any of my burns…"

"You're fine, dear. You're all covered up and looking proper. Don't you fret now, we'll keep an eye on everything. Are you cold?"

"A little."

"Let me turn up the temperature in here a bit. It's a cold blustery day outside for sure."

Norman, Delbert, and Neil loitered in the hallway, watching everyone dashing back and forth. The only one who looked like his clothes fit, Norman was dressed in a black suit with a white shirt and black tie.

"Are you going to a wedding or a funeral?" Neil asked when he saw him.

Delbert, also dressed in a black suit, wore a black-and-white striped shirt that looked a size too big, with a black tie loosely hanging from his neck.

Neil, the scar on his forehead still visible, wore black pants with a blue-and-white checkered shirt, blue sport jacket, and no tie.

A few minutes after 7:00, one of the young nurses came scooting quickly down the hall, clapping her hands and declaring, "They're coming! They're coming! They just got off the elevator! Oh, this is so exciting!"

Mary stepped out of the elevator first while Delmas held the door for her family. Dressed in a simple white dress and white heels, with a pretty ribbon of white and silver in her hair, Mary's eyes sparkled and her face beamed as she waited for Delmas. Grasping a small bouquet of flowers in her hands, she looked down the hall. Her parents Earl and Catherine Moore, looking around, walked up to her.

"Are you ready for this, kiddo?" Catherine barely smiled.

"Not too late to back out, you know," Earl snickered.

"I'm fine. This is going to be really nice," Mary beamed.

Delmas walked up, with Harry and Barbara following closely behind. Harry was sporting a camera which bounced off of him as it dangled from the strap around his neck.

"Where to, Delmas?" Harry inquired.

"Room 412, down there." Delmas pointed toward the mass of nurses and doctors gathered in the hallway.

With Mary's family in tow, she and Delmas made their way down the hall, grinning as they neared Sarah's room.

"Dum Dum Da Dum," sang one of the nurses to the tune of "Here Comes the Bride." Mary giggled, her face turning red. Mildred Hodges grabbed Mary, pulling her toward Sarah's room. Looking over her shoulder, she shook her finger at Delmas and his brothers.

"You boys wait out here till I tell you that you can come in. We're going to get this wedding underway shortly."

Mary waved her family in with her, and the door to Room 412 closed.

"Well, little brother, are you ready?" Norman asked Delmas after lighting another cigarette.

"Absolutely." He grinned, his black suit barely hanging on his thin frame.

While they were talking, Reverend Spindler walked up, greeting everyone. Having previously officiated at the triple funeral in Ava, he was happy to have a pleasant, albeit unusual, task of performing a wedding within Sarah's hospital room.

"Well, Ritter boys," Spindler grinned, putting his hand on the groom's shoulder, "Let's marry off another one of you fellers. Ready, Delmas?"

"Yes, sir," Delmas smiled, shaking hands with the preacher.

Inside the room, Sarah shifted in her bed, grunting quietly as she attempted to get comfortable in the half-sitting position to which her bed had been raised.

"I just can't stand the idea of laying down through this ceremony," she told Mildred before everyone showed up. "Plus Mary's family is here. I think I should be sitting up." So Mildred cranked her bed up a bit, so that Sarah could greet everyone and watch from a better position.

After Mary introduced her family to Sarah, Mildred settled in to checking the ribbon in Mary's hair. The bride-to-be tightly grasped the corsage of artificial red roses and ribbon.

"Here, dear," Mildred held out her hand. "Let me pin that corsage on you."

As Mildred pinned, Mary looked past her to see her mother Catherine chatting with Sarah.

"I'm so sorry to hear of that terrible fire and your injuries, Mrs. Ritter." Catherine extended her hand as she leaned over the rail on Sarah's bed.

"Oh please, call me Sarah. Thank you, Mrs. Moore." Sarah held Catherine's hand, gently patting it. "Mary has certainly been a blessing to me. She's been up here visiting with me a lot, and we sure look forward to having her in the family."

"Well," Catherine shifted as she stood, "I know she's looking forward to this."

Once Mildred adjusted Mary to her liking, she opened the door and stuck her head out.

"Okay, boys, get in here!"

One by one, the men shuffled in, with Mildred directing them where to stand, all the while looking over her shoulder to make sure Sarah could see from her bed. Once everyone got positioned according to Mildred's direction, she stepped out of the room, making sure to leave the door open so that the growing mass of nurses and doctors could watch or at least listen to the proceedings from the hallway. With Mary's brother Harry moving around and snapping pictures, Reverend Spindler called the ceremony to order.

"Dearly beloved, we are gathered this day to join Mary and Delmas in holy matrimony. While we perform this ceremony, not in the house of God but rather in a hospital room, it makes no difference, and makes it no less special. As we know that God said where there are two or more gathered in my name, there I am also. It is very fitting, that while we celebrate the continued healing of Sarah and the entire Ritter family, we now celebrate the joining of these two lives."

Mary and Delmas stood facing each other as Reverend Spindler spoke, looking in each other's eyes. Mary beamed, wrinkling her nose at Delmas playfully. He grinned, winking back at her.

Delbert stood silently to Delmas' right, shifting his weight from one foot to the other and staring at the ground. Barbara stood to Mary's left, quietly watching the proceedings. Earl and Catherine stood near Sarah's bed to watch.

Sarah quietly wiped a tear from her eye.

After a brief exchange of vows, Delmas took Mary's left hand and under Spindler's direction, slipped Mary's ring on her finger. Afterwards, Mary placed Delmas' ring on his finger.

"I now pronounce you husband and wife. What God has joined together, let no man put asunder. You may kiss your bride."

Wasting no time, Delmas and Mary moved toward each other and embraced in a long kiss. The entire hallway, full of doctors, nurses and mobile patients, erupted in cheers and applause while everyone in the room applauded as well.

As people began to slowly leave Sarah's room, Mary leaned over and kissed Sarah on the cheek.

"Mary, thank you so much. I'm so happy that you both chose to do this. I can't tell you how much it means to me." Sarah's eyes teared again.

"We were so happy to do it, Mom," Mary beamed and leaned over and kissed Sarah again.

19

March 19, 1960 – 10:22a.m.
Ava, Missouri

What a nice day today... the first nice day in a long, long time...

Downtown Ava bustled with activity, as mild temperatures and warm sunshine brought out throngs of people, all chatting about the weather and being stuck inside for so long, and wishing each other a pleasant day.

Virginia, dressed in a light jacket over her blouse and jeans, strolled along the sidewalk along the north side of the square. She hadn't walked around the square since mid-October, when she, Dewey, and Gary first got home from Paris, and was lost in her thoughts.

I can do this. I'm sure I can do this. I've got to keep going... Oh, Dewey, how I wish we were walking along together...

"Virginia!"

She jumped at the sound of someone calling her name.

Dear God, someone recognized me.

Her body tensed as she cowered over slightly. Her confidence shaken, she scowled then she stiffly turned right then left to find the source of the yelling.

"Virginia!"

She looked to her left. Walking quickly toward her, Dick and Jack Ritter smiled and waved.

No! Oh God, no! They're going to yell at me!

Virginia began to walk quickly away from the two approaching men. Dick and Jack stopped in their tracks.

"I'll be damned. It is true after all," Dick muttered.

"What's that, Dad?" Jack asked as he watched Virginia hurry away, glancing once over her shoulder.

"Cora told me that she heard at church that word has gotten out that Virginia thinks we all hate her. She thinks we blame her for Dewey dying."

"What?" Jack couldn't believe his ears.

"Yep. She apparently believes that her delay at the window caused Dewey's death, and that we all blame her for it. We need to catch up to her and set her straight. Come on, let's see where she goes. Let's try to talk to her."

Crossing the square, they called out to her, asking her to stop.

"Come on, Virginia, we just want to talk to you for a moment," Jack called out.

Virginia walked more quickly as tears began to stream down her face.

My God, they are after me!

Without looking, she stepped off the sidewalk and darted across the intersection of Washington Avenue and Spurlock Street. A westbound car, taking off from the stop sign on Washington, nearly hit her and honked his horn as she walked quickly across.

"Jesus, she doesn't need to get hurt again, crazy kid." Dick shook his head as they sped up to catch her.

The two men gained on her as she ran along the sidewalk then to her car, fumbling with the handle to get in.

"Virginia, honey, please stop!" Dick called out, by now just five feet behind Virginia as she dove into her car, forgetting that her window was down.

Virginia turned and looked at the men, tears streaming down her face.

"Virginia, honey, you know us. Why did you run from us?" Jack asked as he and Dick leaned over to her open window.

"Because I know you hate me!" Virginia bellowed, "I didn't want you to yell at me. But now that you caught me, I guess you might as well go ahead. I can take it."

"My God, Virginia. You don't need to feel that way." Dick reached out to her but she recoiled. "Honey, we all love you. You are a part of this family…"

"No, I'm not. Not anymore." She looked down, wiping her nose with a hankie she found in her purse.

"Yes, yes you are. That will never change." Dick's voice softened as he leaned in closer to her.

"Virginia, our feelings for you haven't changed none." Jack stepped forward.

"But… but it's my fault… and you all know it… if I hadn't…"

"No, Virginia, it's not your fault." Dick shook his head.

"Yes it is!" Virginia bellowed, crying again. "If I would have jumped sooner, he would still be alive! My Dewey and… and my Gary, they would still be alive! It's my fault! I killed them and now all of you hate me!"

"Virginia, come out of the car and talk to us."

Virginia looked at him and paused.

Oh God, I want a Ritter man to hold me again.

She dropped her head and began to sob uncontrollably.

Dick leaned in and put his arm on her shoulder, patting her softly as she cried. She reached up and held his hand.

"Oh, Dick, I miss him so bad. So bad," she sobbed.

"I know, honey," Dick whispered as she held on to him. "We all do."

"I don't want to live. I just don't want to live," Virginia cried.

"Shhhh now, don't say that," Jack chimed in.

"But it's true!" Virginia yelled as she let go of his hand and pulled away. "I'm so ashamed. I just… I just can't believe I lived and they died! Why? Why? I… I should have… I should have died with them. That's where I belong… dead with them."

"No no no," Dick protested, but Virginia cut him off.

"Yes! Yes, I should have died. I'm sure many in your family wish I would have."

"No, Virginia, it's not true. Like I said, we love you and want you to…"

"No, Dick," Virginia interrupted again. "That's not true and you know it. Look, I appreciate what you're trying to do, and I appreciate you not yelling at me. But I know the truth. I'm not a Ritter anymore.

Goodbye, gentlemen."

She rolled up her window and started her car, quickly backing out without looking. She nearly collided with another car making its trek around the square, leaving Jack and Dick looking at each other.

"Let me talk to her some more," Jack said, starting toward the car.

"No, son." Dick grabbed Jack's arm. "Let her be. At this point, she needs to settle down a bit. Maybe we'll have the chance to talk to her again soon. For now, let's just let her be."

As the two men walked away, from inside the car Virginia looked over and saw them leave. Just before they walked out of sight, Dick looked back at the car again.

As she sat watching, tears streaming down her face, she pulled her hand, the one Dick held, up to her nose. She could smell Dick's cologne on it from holding her.

Oh, Dewey...

The car behind her honked, and she turned onto Washington Avenue to drive back to the Dye house. For Virginia, the pleasant spring day no longer mattered. Oblivious to the pleasant breeze, the sound of birds chirping, and the lingering soreness in her hip, she concentrated on getting back to her parents' home on Curry Avenue.

I can't stay here. I've got to leave. I can't stay in this town. Too many memories. Too much pain. I don't want to see them again. I know they hate me. I don't care what they said, they hate me. I'm not a Ritter anymore. I never can be again. Oh, Dewey. Why did you have to die? I can't stay here in this town with so many memories. I can't even drive past the cemetery. It hurts too much. I've got to leave.

The words repeated over and over again in her head as tears once again welled up in her eyes.

Finally reaching the safety of her home, she found her mother sitting at the kitchen table cutting coupons out of the newspaper.

"Mama?" Virginia got her mother's attention as she sat down next to her at the table.

Lula looked up from her coupons and saw the tears streaming down her daughter's face.

"Virginia, honey, what happened?"

"Mama, I ran into Dick and Jack Ritter while I was walking around the square."

"Oh, honey, they must have been thrilled to see you!"

"But Mama, you don't understand. The Ritters hate me. They blame me for everything. For Dewey and Gary… everything! If it wasn't for me, those two would still be here!"

Lula reached over to Virginia, trying to calm her as she got more frantic.

"Virginia, we've talked about this. No one blames you!"

"No Mama, it's true! It's my fault! I should have jumped sooner!" Virginia jumped up, crying harder. "They would still be alive if I would have just jumped sooner!"

Lula jumped up and grabbed Virginia, wrapping her arms around.

"Virginia, honey, calm down. Now did Jack and Dick tell you they hate you?"

"…No…"

"What did they say when they saw you?"

"Dick… Dick held… Dick reached into the car and… and held my hand…" Virginia sobbed harder.

"Shhh, baby… Now when Dick held on to you, did he say that the family hated you? That it was your fault?"

"…No…"

"What did he say?"

"He… he said that they… he said that they love me and want me to… to… to still be a part of the family…"

"I kinda thought so. Virginia, do you believe him?"

Virginia didn't respond. She just held her mom tighter as she cried.

"Virginia, honey? I said do you believe him?"

Virginia pulled away from her mom, grabbing the hanky from her pocket to wipe her nose. Lula stood in front of Virginia with her hands folded, waiting for an answer.

After wiping her nose, Virginia collected herself and looked at Lula.

"No, Mama, I don't believe him. No one can convince me this was not my fault. I can't… I can't stay here, Mama. There are too many memories. Too many people who know what happened. Too many Ritters and relations to worry about running into. Mama, I've got to leave this town."

"Are you sure, Virginia?"

"Yes, Mama. I'm sure." Virginia sat down again at the table as her mother returned to her seat as well, taking Virginia's hand, still listening. "All I've ever wanted was to be a wife and a mother. And it was wonderful with Dewey and Gary. Dewey was my true love. I fell in love with him when I was fourteen and never got over it. And he will always be my true love. But I've got to go somewhere else. I've got to try again."

Lula let out a sigh, let go of Virginia's hand, and took off her glasses.

"Yes, dear, I think you are right. A new beginning here would be difficult. This is a good town, filled with good people that we love. But it's all too fresh, all too painful."

Virginia nodded.

Putting her glasses back on, Lula took Virginia's hand once again.

"Honey, your father and I have decided we need to move away, too."

Virginia gasped as her eyes grew large.

"Seriously, Mama? You guys want to leave Ava?"

"It's all too fresh for us too, honey. I don't think you realize how much we loved Dewey and Gary. We've kept our grieving from you because we wanted to put on a brave face while you healed. We know you've been through a lot. But your father has cried so many times, and Donnal misses Dewey so badly. You remember how Dewey spent so much time with him, talking to him about the Air Force. Now he wants to go join up because of everything Dewey told him, and also to honor his memory. We've all been hurting over this. I loved Sarah and Orville. And I've had to answer lots of questions in town, about how you are doing, and are the stories true about what happened that night. It's been exhausting. They all have meant well, and there's no malice in their questions. This is a good town and they are all good loving people, and they just want to know. It's just too much. We can't go by the cemetery, either, dear. It hurts too much."

Lula paused for a moment, catching her breath.

"Your father and I want to sell this house and move away. Not too far; we still have lots of family in this area. But we are thinking about finding a place in Ozark and settling there. Starting over."

The two women stared at each other for a moment. Virginia was speechless.

I never thought about how much this hurt them, too...

After several seconds, Virginia finally spoke.

"When do you guys plan to move, Mama?"

"Your dad was waiting for you and me to have a talk. Now that we've had this chat, I believe we will list the house next week. There are a couple of places in Ozark that we have already looked at, so I think we will get one of them, if they are still available."

Virginia looked down at the table. Lula squeezed her hand.

"You wanna come with us to Ozark, dear?"

Virginia sighed.

"No Mama. I'm sorry, but I don't think Ozark is far enough away."

"Honey, where are you thinking about going?"

"I was thinking maybe Roswell..."

Virginia's sister Pauline lived in Roswell, New Mexico with her husband Stanley and their toddler son, Jerry Lee, who was just a few months past his second birthday.

"I sent a letter to Pauline a couple of weeks ago," Virginia confessed, "and I asked her if I could perhaps come out there, maybe help with little Jerry Lee while she works. She says there's lots of work available out there, something I could find to do eventually..."

She looked up at her mother.

"I think it might be a good place to start over, Mama."

Lula looked down for a moment then looked back up at Virginia. Smiling weakly, she squeezed Virginia's hand again.

"Yes, dear. It sounds like a good idea. We'll pay for your bus fare to get out there."

The two women stood up from the table and moved toward each other with arms out to hug.

"I'm gonna miss you and Daddy, Mama."

"We'll miss you, too, dear."

One week later, Virginia was on a bus headed west.

20

For Sarah, February became March and March became April from the confines of her hospital bed. The days, nights, weeks and weekends were filled with changes of dressings, slow walks to the bathroom, and above all, the constant presence of intense pain. Sitting caused pain. Lying in bed caused pain. Walking caused pain. Every movement, every breath, every moment of the day the pain held her captive, strangled her, and drove her into the depths of despair.

She hated the pain medications, the barrage of aspirin, along with the decreased amounts of Demerol and morphine. But mostly she hated the time lost when she succumbed to the stupor of the drugs. All the medication was supposed to help her but only deadened her senses, not the pain.

When her mind was clear and the pain sharp and constant, she lay in bed and wept quietly. It had only been less than six months since The Fire, since losing her beloved Orville, since hearing Dewey scream, "Neil, I'm burning alive!" and since learning that dreadful night that little Gary had also perished in the flames. She knew that even if she was instantly healed and could leave the hospital, there was nowhere to go. No home waiting for her, no closet with her clothes, and no husband's hand to hold.

April 6, 1960 – 9:40 p.m.
St. John's Hospital, Room 412

"Mom, I think I'm going to get a coffee. Do you need anything?" Wanda asked, walking to the door.

"Yes, I sure do," Sarah uttered quietly, looking up instead of toward Wanda.

Wanda stopped and looked back at Sarah, continuing to stare at the ceiling.

"Mom?"

No answer.

"Mom? Honey, what do you need?"

Sarah blinked, glanced at Wanda, then looked back at the ceiling, past it to somewhere else.

"I need someone to take me back to October 26th and let me stay right there."

Her voice began to quiver.

"I'd have my Orville, my Dewey, my Gary, my home, my life."

She turned toward Wanda, tears running down her cheeks.

"I want my life back."

Wanda, tears in her eyes, walked back to the bed and leaned over to gently hold her mother as she wept.

"I'm so sorry, Mom. I want them all back, too. I wish we could turn back time and all of us be together again. If I could, I would."

Sarah loosened her hold on Wanda, and the two women separated.

"I know, dear." Sarah wiped her eyes then looked back at the ceiling. "I'm sorry, it just came out. I miss them so bad. I miss havin' my home, my chickens. I miss that drafty old house."

Speedy and Wanda glanced at each other as Sarah let out a heavy sigh.

"I'm going to say something, kids, and I'm not sure it's going to make much sense. But here goes, so be patient with me."

She didn't look at either of her visitors. She kept staring at the ceiling.

"I have these burns on me, these daily reminders of what happened. I live with the pain of knowing what happened that night, and who we lost. But I have another kind of burning, deep down inside me. The burning to keep going. Does that make sense?"

She looked at Wanda, then Speedy, each one responding with silent nods.

"I'm going to get through this. I'm going to keep livin'." Sarah turned to Wanda again. "Someday, I'm going to have my own place again, with clothes in my closet, and my own pots and pans. And I'll have company come visit me. And then…"

Sarah paused for a moment, turning to stare at the ceiling again.

"And then some day… some day when I'm strong again… somebody is going to drive me to Ava… and I'm going to put flowers on the graves of my boys… my precious boys…"

April 15 – 6:50 p.m.
Norman Ritter's house, Springfield, Missouri

Norman and Jerry were enjoying a Friday night together at home when the phone rang. Jerry was the first to reach it.

"Hello?"

"Mrs. Ritter?"

"Yes."

"This is Doctor Charles Lockhart from St. John's. Would Mr. Ritter happen to be available?"

"Yes, just a moment." Jerry pulled the phone away. "Norman? It's Doctor Lockhart."

Norman jumped up and grabbed the phone.

"Hi, Doctor, this is Norman."

"Hi, Norman, please accept my apologies for bothering you this evening."

"It's no bother at all," Norman reassured. "Is Mom okay?"

"Well yes, but I wanted to ask if you could come to the hospital this coming Monday afternoon. I have an idea, an opportunity for her, and I want to discuss it with you and her. Could you be at the hospital around 4:00?"

"Absolutely, Doc. I'll be there. I'll be anxious to hear what you have to say."

"Great. Thanks, Norman. I'll see you and Mrs. Ritter Monday afternoon."

"See you then."

Norman turned to Jerry.

"Looks like I'll be at the hospital before I go to work Monday night. The doc says he's got something up his sleeve for Mom."

"Wonder what it could be." Jerry frowned.

"He said it was an opportunity. To me that sounds like a good thing. Guess we'll find out Monday!"

April 18
St. John's Hospital, Room 412

Norman was seated in Sarah's room by 3:30, visiting in advance of Doctor Lockhart's visit. At 4:03, a gentle knock on the door announced the doctor's arrival.

"Well, I was almost on time!" Lockhart laughed, looking down at his watch.

Norman stood up and shook hands with Lockhart as Sarah struggled to sit up a little in bed.

"Hi, Mrs. Ritter." Doctor Lockhart turned to Sarah after shaking hands with Norman. "How are you feeling this afternoon?"

"Well… I'm hurting plenty, but I'm sure happy to have a clear mind by not being on those pain medicines."

"Yes, ma'am, I sure understand. Before we visit, may I take a look under your bandages?"

"Of course, Doctor." Sarah pushed her blanket and sheet down as Norman got up to close the door.

After carefully checking all of Sarah's burns, the doctor made a couple of notes on the sheet on his clipboard, then settled down in the chair on Sarah's left. Norman pulled up a chair at the foot of the bed.

Sarah reached over and grabbed the doctor's hand.

"Well, Miss Sarah, your burns are doing as well as can be expected. We are happy to have no signs of infection. But the reason I wanted to talk with both of you is I feel like we have perhaps done about all we can for you here, based on the capabilities of this hospital, our equipment, and staff. Naturally I would love to continue to take care of you, but I think there are others who could do more for you."

"More? What do you mean, Doctor?" Sarah's brow furrowed.

"Well, there are facilities that specialize in burn treatment. And right now, there are some clinical trials going on and treatment procedures being developed that show great promise. I did some checking, and right now the closest burn unit participating in the trials is at the university hospital in Columbia."

"Columbia, Missouri?" Sarah's eyes widened.

"Yes, just about three hours up the road."

Sarah turned and looked at Norman, who appeared deep in thought.

"Norman, what's on your mind?" she inquired.

Norman looked up, glanced at his mom, then turned to Doctor Lockhart.

"Could you help me understand this idea of clinical trials and this development of procedures? The first thing that jumps into my head is guinea pig. Are they going to be experimenting on my mother?"

"A valid question, Norman." Lockhart smiled. "Clinical trials are not random experimentation. There are new methods for burn treatment that have been proposed, but the methods have to be used in real life to make sure they are suitable. So clinical trials are set up under controlled conditions to test the methods, and then procedures are developed that other medical professionals can use to get the same results."

Lockhart turned to Sarah.

"They will perform some new procedures on you, procedures to treat your worst burns, then will closely monitor those areas to evaluate the success of the procedures."

"I think I understand." Norman nodded. "No offense intended. It just sounded kinda different."

"No offense taken, Norman. I'm glad you voiced a concern."

Sarah turned to Lockhart.

"You mentioned procedures, Doctor." Sarah squeezed his hand, "Can you tell me more about what they would be doing?"

"Of course." Lockhart smiled. "Miss Sarah, you recall we talked before about the three degrees of burns, and how your worst ones are third degree? And there's major damage there, right? That's why it hurts so bad."

Sarah nodded.

"Well, at Columbia, they are doing something called skin grafting. They take good skin from another part of your body and install it, or graft it, on the burn, to help the damaged skin begin to build new tissue. Your skin has been so badly damaged by fire, it is having a hard time generating new tissue to heal those places on your body. Skin grafting has been around for a long time. Now, through this research, the methods are advancing and the success rates of getting the grafted skin to work and produce healthy replacement tissue are greatly improved. They are also using water baths to soften the skin and keep it clean and healthy. Lots of things going on. So to me, this sounds very promising, and as the doctor who's been taking care of you and watching your degree of healing, honestly, it is my recommendation that you take Columbia up on its offer."

Sarah looked back at Norman.

"Well, that would be wonderful, Doctor," Norman spoke up. "But I'm a little concerned about cost. It's going to be hard enough to pay the medical bill here. I don't know how any of us could pay for her stay at Columbia, however long that would be."

"Well, that's the best part, Norman." Doctor Lockhart smiled. "If Sarah signs up to participate in the clinical trials, it doesn't cost anything."

"What?" Sarah looked as if she was going to climb out of the bed.

"Yes!" Doctor Lockhart turned to Sarah and squeezed her hand. "Mrs. Ritter, if you agree to do this, it's free. And you'll be part of something that's going to help the treatment of burn patients for generations. You'll help in the advancement of burn treatment procedures and methods."

Still holding Lockhart's hand, Sarah turned to Norman.

"Norman, what do you think? It sounds like a great deal to me." Sarah sounded hopeful for the first time since the night of The Fire. She then turned back to Lockhart.

"I'm guessing some of these procedures are going to hurt a bit, aren't they, Doctor Lockhart?"

"Well, I won't lie to you, Sarah. It does cause discomfort in the places where the healthy skin is harvested. This won't be a pain-free experience. But you're hurting now, and as I said, we have done about all we can do here. But in Columbia, they can take you to the next level. I believe they can heal you up enough so that someday you'll walk out of that hospital and get back to living your life."

Sarah's eyes welled up with tears.

"And you know something else, Miss Sarah?" Lockhart continued, gently squeezing her hand. "The day you walk out of that hospital, I want to be there to see it."

"Oh, you sweet man." Sarah smiled as a single tear ran down her right cheek.

"It sounds really good, Mom." Norman smiled. "Doc, what about us coming up to visit? We won't be able to keep vigil like we've done here, but we will want to come up and see her whenever we can."

"Of course." Lockhart nodded. "Anyone from the family will be welcome at any time. They have some specific requirements, I believe, because of their procedures. You will most likely have to wear protective clothing, stuff like that. But you'll be welcome. Don't worry about that."

Sarah and Norman looked at each other.

"I say let's do it," Sarah said.

"Doctor, one other question: how do we get her there?" Norman asked.

Lockhart shook his head.

"You don't have to worry about that. She will be transported there by ambulance. Not one of ours, they will actually drive down in one of their nice big rigs to come get her."

"Hey, that almost sounds like one of those limousines!" Sarah laughed.

Doctor Lockhart looked at her and grinned.

"It'll be a comfy ride, believe me." Lockhart squeezed Sarah's hand. "You'll be well taken care of."

"Well, Doc," Norman said, smiling, "it sounds like we are on board. How do we make this happen? What's the timeline?"

Lockhart let go of Sarah's hand and grabbed his clipboard.

"I've got the papers right here. And I've already talked with the burn unit in Columbia. If you both are in agreement, you can sign these forms and they can come get her on May 1."

"Wow, that's quick!" Sarah beamed, "I really want to do this."

"Okay, Doc, let's get this signed and underway," Norman said as he got up to come to Lockhart's side of the bed.

After a few strokes of the pen, both Norman and Sarah had all the paperwork signed.

"Excellent. I think this is truly the right way to go. You'll be in good hands, Mrs. Ritter."

"Doctor Lockhart, I can't thank you enough for taking such good care of me." Sarah grabbed his hand again, tears welling up in her eyes. "And thank you for taking care of my Orville. I know it was a short time, and I hear there wasn't much you could do. But it means a lot."

Clearing his throat, Lockhart put his hand over Sarah's.

"Mrs. Ritter, it's been my pleasure and honor to take care of you. And it was an honor to care for Mr. Ritter in his last few days. You've got some great kids," Lockhart winked at Norman, "and I think you're quite a special lady."

"Thank you, dear." Sarah squeezed his hand again then let him pull away as Norman came over to shake hands.

"Thank you Doctor." Norman grinned as he shook Lockhart's hand.

As Lockhart left the room, Norman settled into the doctor's seat. He and Sarah sighed at the same time.

"Well, Mom, this sounds good. And don't you worry, we'll come up to see you."

"I know, son." Sarah patted his hand. "You know, I'm actually kinda excited about this. A little scared to be so far away, and a little scared of this skin grafting thing. But we gotta do something to heal these burns. Sounds like Columbia has the plan."

May 1
St. John's Hospital

As promised, a large ambulance from Columbia's university hospital arrived at St. John's with orders to transport Sarah. After transferring her to a gurney for moving, all the nurses on duty on 4 West came to wish her well. Sarah did her best to hug each one.

"Girls, we've all become family since I've been here for so long," Sarah told the crowd of nurses.

"We love you, Miss Sarah!" came the response from several of them.

Sarah waved as the attendants wheeled her down the hall to the elevators. Within minutes, she was in the ambulance and on her way to Columbia.

21

May 23, 6:30 a.m.
University Hospital, Columbia, Missouri

Sarah jolted awake as the lights came on in her room. She blinked several times, trying to clear the cobwebs of sleep out of her head while her nurse came bouncing in.

"Good morning, Miss Sarah! I'm Olivia and I will be taking care of you today!"

"Good morning, dear," Sarah yawned, then squinted when Olivia opened the curtains, blasting the room with sunlight.

Lying on her side, Sarah watched the nurse preparing the morning medications for injection into her IV tubing.

Left side today...

May 23 was left-side day. The day before had been right-side day. And May 24 would be right-side day again. The large patches of skin harvested from the backs of her thighs and buttocks left painful open wounds. To help those open places heal, she had been forced to sleep on alternating sides since the original skin grafting procedure.

"Olivia, I hate to ask, but do you have any idea when I might be able to lie on my back again?"

"Let's take a look," Olivia said, walking around to the other side of the bed. She pulled back the sheet and light blanket covering

Sarah, then leaned over and gently removed the bandages.

"Things are looking good back here, Miss Sarah. We will clean them again and put fresh bandages on. But it won't be too long before you can lie on your back."

"Thank you, dear," Sarah answered, her stomach growling.

"Sounds like you are ready for breakfast!" Olivia giggled.

"I sure am." Sarah smiled. "The way you all have been feeding me, I think my appetite has grown. And that's really saying something!"

Olivia giggled again as she walked around the bed to Sarah's left side and held out her hands.

"Well, let's get you cleaned up. By the time we are done and have you in a fresh gown and the bed sheets changed out, it'll be time for breakfast. Then you can look forward to this morning's warm water bath."

"Yes, dear, I do enjoy those. They feel good on this old lady." Sarah winced as she carefully rolled out of bed. Olivia leaned over and slipped Sarah's house shoes on her feet. With the nurse still holding her hands, Sarah took her first steps of the new day.

11:45 a.m.
Silver Lining Café, Roswell, NM

Virginia caught her breath as she looked up from wiping down a table.

Good God, he's huge.

Walking in the door with a couple of buddies, a tall, broad-shouldered man barely fit through the doorframe. Standing at the front waiting for the hostess to seat the group, his eyes met Virginia's. He smiled and winked. Virginia instantly blushed and turned away, walking back to the kitchen.

"You've got Table 5, Virginia," Marge the hostess blurted out as she blew into the kitchen. "Watch out for that really tall gorilla in the group. He likes to flirt."

"I saw him. He winked at me." Virginia giggled.

"Be careful, girlie. Charmers are usually hiding something," Marge grumbled as she blew out of the kitchen again.

Virginia cleared her throat, straightened her apron and checked her hair, grabbed menus then walked confidently out of the kitchen and to Table 5.

"Hello, gentlemen, I'm Virginia and I'll be your waitress. Can I get you something to drink while you look over the menu?"

"Virginia! That's a nice name," the tall man bellowed.

She smiled and took out her pencil and ticket pad. The other two men ordered iced tea.

"You don't have any beer here, do ya?" The tall man looked up with a smirk.

"No, I'm sorry, we don't serve beer here. I've got tea, coffee, milk, and sodas. And water of course."

"Water is fine."

"Okay, I'll be back with your drinks."

As Virginia turned and walked back to the counter to make drinks for the three, she felt the tall man's eyes on her from behind. It felt strangely exhilarating, and she began to struggle with it.

He's looking at me. I know he's looking at me. I haven't been looked at by a man since... since Dewey.

Digging into the ice machine, she couldn't help herself and looked back at the table. Sure enough, he was looking at her and smiling. She quickly looked away.

Should I feel guilty? I mean, I'm a married woman. I'm Dewey Ritter's wife... no, wait... wait a minute... no, I'm not... not anymore...

Virginia cleared her throat, choking something back, and let out a deep sigh.

After the three men finished their meals, Virginia returned to the table to refill their drinks and drop off their tickets.

"Why don't you put your phone number on my ticket?" the tall man bellowed.

Virginia smirked.

"I don't think so. I don't even know you, mister."

"Well, I'm Billy Joe McCormack. And you are Virginia. There. We know each other."

"Nice try, fella," she said, smiling, "y'all can pay Marge at the front counter. Thanks for coming in."

Blushing, she felt him looking at her again as she walked away.

That night, at the dinner table, she told Pauline and Stan about the huge customer.

"How big do you think this guy was?" Stan asked.

"Oh goodness, he had to be about seven feet tall," Virginia beamed. "He towered over his friends, and they towered over me. He was easily a foot taller than Dewey. I felt his eyes following me the whole time."

Stan looked at Pauline and winked.

"How did that make you feel?" Pauline reached over and touched Virginia's arm.

Virginia looked at Pauline then Stan then Pauline again. She shifted in her chair, crossing her legs.

"I… I haven't felt… it felt good. Like lightning bolts hitting me. He was huge… and handsome… and… and… he flirted with me. I haven't been flirted with since… since, uh… since Dewey's been gone."

"Nothing wrong with flirting, sis." Pauline patted her arm. "Just be careful. You're still kinda vulnerable, you know. Lightning bolts are nice, but, you know, be careful."

"I know," Virginia said quietly as she took a sip of tea.

Two days later, when Billy Joe returned to the café, she wrote her phone number on an extra ticket and gave it to him.

22

May 27, 7:10 a.m.
Norman Ritter's house, Springfield, Missouri

"Neil?"

Jerry sat looking at the wide-eyed, bewildered soul sitting across the table from her.

Bless his heart. He's so tired.

"Neil?"

No response. He kept staring off to his left, looking deep into something, somewhere.

"Neil, honey, do you want to talk about it?"

He blinked.

He blinked again.

He finally turned and looked at her, eyes welling up with tears.

"I… I was back there… again… in that burning house. Dewey… Dewey was screaming again. I… I tried to get to him… again."

Neil looked down, a single tear dropping to his lap.

"I'm… I'm getting to the point where I… I hate going to sleep. I hate dreaming about that night. I hate having to go back to…"

He began staring off to the left again.

"… to that house."

Jerry sighed.

"Neil, what can I do to help?"

Neil turned back to Jerry.

"Nothing, sis. Not a damn thing."

8:45p.m.
Estes Truck Stop, Roswell, NM

Virginia tried to enjoy her steak dinner despite the noise around her. At the counter, two drivers argued loudly over politics while cramming food in their mouths. Across the diner, the jukebox attempted to play "Cathy's Clown" by the Everly Brothers, but the record kept skipping. The family on vacation two booths behind her had a toddler that liked to scream when he wanted another bite of food. And then across the table from her, there sat Billy Joe, happily chewing his steak and french fries with his mouth open.

"Yer awful quiet over there, lil lady," Billy Joe said immediately after shoving a roll in his mouth.

"Oh sorry." Virginia cracked an uncomfortable smile. "This steak is really good. I was just enjoying it."

"Yup, this is good, ain't it! Thought you'd like the food here. Lil different from that joint you work at," he snickered.

"Yes. Yes it is." Virginia looked nervously around the room.

"So that house I picked you up at. Who lives there with you?"

"That's my sister Pauline's house. She and her husband Stanley. I moved in with them when I came out west."

"So tell me again," Billy Joe bellowed, "what's the name of that little hick town in Missouri you come from?"

"Ava."

"What did you do there?"

"Well, when I was younger I worked as a waitress at the little café they had at Ava Drug."

"Okay. Then what were you doing there when you decided to move here?"

Virginia took a quick drink of tea.

"Well… I guess that needs a little explanation… I was married. And I had a little boy, his name was Gary. My husband was in the Air Force. We lived in Paris for quite a while."

"Paris, Texas? I've been there!"

"No. Paris, France. We were overseas. That's where Gary was born."

"Oh. So where's this husband and son? Did you leave them behind in Missouri?"

"No."

Virginia stared at her plate.

How do I say this?

She looked up to find Billy Joe looking at her.

"When Dewey-"

"Dewey? This hick's name was Dewey?" Billy Joe bellowed laughingly.

Virginia sighed.

"Yes, his name was Dewey. And he was a good man."

Billy Joe scowled.

"Sorry. Keep going."

"When Dewey was discharged from the Air Force, we came back to Ava. We stayed with my parents for about a week. Then we moved over to stay with his parents for a while. They lived in a little rundown farmhouse. The plan was to eventually move to Springfield and Dewey was going to get a job. He was into electronics."

Billy Joe stared at her, his arms crossed.

"But… the first night we were at his parents' place, the house caught fire while we were asleep."

Virginia paused and took another drink.

"I've hardly spoken of this since that night."

"I'm listening," Billy Joe said, his arms still crossed.

Virginia looked down at the table.

"Well… it was awful. The place was going up around us. We were all trapped upstairs. We couldn't get down because the stairs were on fire."

She looked up at Billy Joe as tears welled up in her eyes.

"Dewey was holding Gary. I was afraid to jump. So he… he pushed me out the window. I fell and landed on a tree root. It broke my pelvis. I… I never lost consciousness though."

"So did this Dewey fella jump next with the kid?"

"No. I don't know what exactly happened. They said the floor must have caved in. He… he fell… through the floor… with little Gary. They… they both died in the fire."

Virginia grabbed a napkin and wiped her eyes.

"So yer a widow, then! A young widow!" Billy Joe still had his arms crossed in front of him.

"Yes. And there's something else."

"What?"

"Well, I was pregnant again, with our second child. But… but… when I landed and hit that tree root and busted my pelvis, it…"

She stopped and took a breath.

"It what? What happened?"

"The little baby died. When we got to the hospital in Springfield, they told me that they didn't detect a heartbeat. They said the baby died on impact."

"Was it a boy or girl?"

"I don't know."

"Hmmm." Billy Joe uncrossed his arms and took a drink of tea. "That's too bad. A young pretty thing like you widowed and her kids dead."

My God, how can he be such a harsh person? Doesn't he understand how badly this hurt? Doesn't he understand how awful this was? I hope this gets better.

"It was awful. When I got out of the hospital and healed at my parents' place, I decided I couldn't stay in that little town anymore. Everyone knew what had happened. I felt their eyes on me. And I ended up running into some of Dewey's family once. I just couldn't stay there. So I moved out here to stay with my sister and her husband and their little boy."

"Start a new life, right?" Billy Joe crammed another roll in his mouth.

"Right." Virginia smiled weakly.

"Well, little lady, feel free to leave all that behind." Billy Joe winked. "You've got a new life right in front of you."

"I hope so."

"Yep. So you just forget about dear ole hick Dewey and them kids. They're gone."

Oh God, he's so rude. I hope this gets better…

10:00 p.m.
University Hospital, Columbia, Missouri

Sarah lay in bed awake, tears streaming down her face.

Oh, Orville, I feel so lost without you. I'm trying to be strong. I'm trying my best to get through this. I always felt like I could get through anything as long as you were here with me. If I could just hold your hand, like we used to...

We should have sold that house. We should have just gotten away from it. None of this would have happened. I wouldn't be here with all these bandages and there wouldn't be any daily pokings and I'd have my kids and a house and Dewey and Gary would still be here...

She let out a long sigh, wiped her eyes, and slowly reached for her cup of water. Everything hurt. Her burns hurt, reminding her of that night. Her thighs and buttocks hurt, from the harvesting of fresh skin to graft to the burns that reminded her of that night. Her eyes stung from the salt in the tears from crying over the pain that reminded her of that night.

After a quick sip of water, she let out another long sigh.

I have to keep going. We still have eight kids living, Orville. And grandbabies. And there will be more. Delmas and Mary are already expecting a young'un. Denney, Teresa, and Jimmy are all getting bigger. The family is growing, Orville, and they need a granny. So I gotta keep going. I gotta... I... I gotta keep going...

11:00 p.m.
Roswell, NM

Billy Joe pulled into the driveway of Pauline and Stanley's house, revved the engine, then shut it off.

"Bet they heard that engine inside the house!" he snickered as he turned toward Virginia.

Virginia smiled weakly, her eyes shifting from Billy to the front door of the house then back to Billy again as she squirmed in her seat.

"Come here, little lady."

She scooted over toward Billy by about an inch.

He grabbed her and pulled her close, kissing her roughly.

Oh dear God, he's kissing me. Dewey never was this rough. I shouldn't be kissing him. I'm a married woman!

Virginia pushed against Billy Joe, which made him pull her in closer. She put her hands against his chest and pushed. His grip tightened as he tried to force his tongue into her mouth.

Ugh. Please stop. I don't want to do this. Please stop.

She pushed hard against him, and he lurched forward, pinning her underneath him. He started grabbing at her blouse, trying to find the buttons.

Virginia quickly turned her head to get away from his mouth and screamed, "Noooooo!"

Panting, Billy Joe sat up as Virginia scrambled, grabbed her purse, and opened the door.

"What the hell is the matter with you, woman? I buy you a nice meal and this is what I git in return?"

"I'm sorry!" Virginia cried. "I'm just not ready yet. I'm just…"

"They're dead, lady! You can't bring them back!"

Crying, Virginia slammed the door and ran to the house as Billy Joe started his truck and backed out the driveway. Stepping in the door, Virginia turned to see the truck in the road, with Billy Joe scowling at her. Tears streaming down her face, she watched as he floored the gas pedal, spinning the tires, then took off down the road.

She closed the door, leaned against it, buried her face in her hands and sobbed.

23

July 9, 1960
En route to Columbia, Missouri

"Good God, son, are we almost there?"

Delbert snickered as he looked in the rear-view mirror to see Neil leaning forward after asking his question.

The three-hour drive to Columbia to visit Sarah tested the fortitude of the passengers and driver, none of whom were accustomed to long journeys. Dorothy snuggled up next to Delbert in the front seat as he drove. Neil and LaVonne were happy with the back seat, which worked out well for Delbert, who had a tendency to get carsick while riding in the back seat. Both couples, recently engaged, decided to make the drive to the burn hospital to share the good news with Sarah in hopes that it would lift her spirits to see family. This was their first visit to their mother since her move to the hospital in Columbia, and they were anxious to learn of the progress being made in the healing of her burns.

Upon arriving at the hospital, Delbert took the lead as they checked in at the front desk.

"Ma'am, we are here to see Sarah Ritter. She's healing from wounds from a fire."

"Yes, sir." The nurse nodded as she looked through her registry for Sarah's name and room number. "Oh, I see she's on the fifth floor. That's a special care ward. Are you all family?" She looked at the four of them.

"Yes, ma'am, Neil and me are her sons, and these ladies are our fiancés," Delbert answered, nodding at Neil, LaVonne, and Dorothy.

"Oh, well congratulations! The elevators are down the hall to your right. When you get to the fifth floor, check in at the desk across from the elevators. There will be a short orientation and you'll have to wear protective clothing to visit Mrs. Ritter. Your mother is in a special room with restrictions, so please take note of the instructions you receive during orientation."

"Very well, ma'am. Thank you." Delbert nodded as they began to walk down the hall toward the elevators.

Stepping into the elevator, Dorothy was perplexed.

"Delbert, if we have to wear protective clothing, and I assume that includes gloves, how are we going to show your mom our rings?"

"I don't know." Delbert shrugged.

"Maybe we can ask to see if we can remove the gloves for a moment to show her," LaVonne chimed in.

"Let's ask when we get there," Neil said.

As promised, another check-in station awaited the foursome upon their arrival on the fifth floor. Once again, Delbert stepped up as spokesperson for the group.

"Ma'am, we are here to see Mrs. Ritter. The lady at the front desk told us to check in with you when we got up here."

"Yes, sir, she called as soon as you all got on the elevator. I'm Linda Adams and I'll help you all get ready to visit Mrs. Ritter. Please come with me to the orientation room."

The group followed Nurse Adams to a small room across from the waiting area. The room, bleak with bright overhead lights, white walls, and a simple round table and chairs, immediately caused a chill in Dorothy and LaVonne. The table had only four chairs.

"Ladies, you go ahead and sit. Me and Neil will stand," Delbert said.

Once everyone settled in, with Delbert and Neil standing behind their respective fiancés, Nurse Adams began to speak.

"As you're all quite aware, Mrs. Ritter has some serious burns from the fire. She is here because we are performing clinical trials on some new procedures in the treatment of burns like hers. We are giving her water baths each day and performing debridement on the wounds, which is quite painful but extremely necessary to promote healing. We have also performed skin grafts. Are you familiar with the idea of skin grafts?"

All four shook their heads.

"Skin grafts have been around for some time, but we are making progress with new methods," Nurse Adams continued. "We harvest healthy skin from a location on the body. Usually this is in areas where perhaps the skin may be looser, or fatty, and we also choose discreet locations. On Mrs. Ritter, we have harvested skin from the backs of her thighs and her buttocks. This skin has been placed, or grafted, within the most severely burned areas, to promote the generation of new skin."

All four family members nodded their heads but said nothing.

"With third-degree burns like Mrs. Ritter has, the damage is deep and tissue destruction is extensive. So with the use of skin grafts, we have an opportunity to take fresh tissue from some location on the patient's body, graft that skin into the location, and with proper care, the skin will regenerate, create new tissue, and heal the wound."

Neil shook his head.

"That's amazing, Nurse. I knew you all were doing something special for her, but I had no idea how extensive it was."

"Yes, Mr. Ritter, it's pretty intense," Nurse Adams answered. "This hospital is on the leading edge and working alongside other hospitals across the country on these clinical trials. Your mother is helping us pioneer new methods to treat future burn patients."

"That's fantastic!" Delbert blurted out.

"Nurse," Dorothy spoke up, "I understand there is some protective clothing we will have to wear?"

"Yes, that was the next thing we need to talk about." Nurse Adams adjusted in her chair. "As you might expect, with open wounds and skin grafts, germs and infections are the enemy. Mrs. Ritter is in a protected space in which we change the highly filtered air several times per hour, and we keep a close eye on how much contact she has with anyone. I'm afraid you will not be permitted to touch her and you will be required to wear protective clothing. Booties over your shoes, protective suits, and gloves."

"Well, the reason I asked," Dorothy said, "We've recently gotten engaged. LaVonne and I were hoping we would be able to show Sarah our rings."

The nurse smiled.

"Yes, but only for a moment. You may remove your gloves to show her briefly, but they must be put back on and all protective gear must remain for the duration of your visit. We take the risk of infection quite seriously."

"Thank you." Dorothy smiled weakly.

"So let's get your visit underway!" Nurse Adams smiled, rising from the table, "Come with me to the next room and I'll get you the protective clothing you need."

The group arose and moved to the next room. The left side was lined with lockers, each with a number on them. Long benches sat in front of the lockers. On the right side of the room were several closets with labels above them, describing their contents. Nurse Adams opened one of the closets and began pulling out bodysuits.

"If this was wintertime, we would ask you all to leave your coats in one of these lockers," Nurse Adams noted as she handed the protective suits to the foursome, who by then were sitting on the benches. "I do need to ask you to leave your purses in here, ladies. The lockers behind you have keys in them. Pick an open locker, put your purses in there, close it, lock it, and keep the key with you. The purses will be secure till you get back."

Dorothy and LaVonne followed the nurse's instructions, and Dorothy gave Delbert the key.

"You be the keeper of the key," she said, winking.

Quickly the four got dressed in their protective gear under the watchful eye of Nurse Adams. When they were finally geared up, she looked them over, made a few adjustments, then directed them to the door behind her.

"This is how we get to her room. You will now be walking through a sterilized area. Try to refrain from touching your face then touching something else."

Nurse Adams walked them down the hall to Sarah's room. She tapped gently on the door as she opened it.

"Miss Sarah? Are you awake?"

"Yes, honey, I'm awake." A familiar voice was heard from within the room.

"I have some visitors for you!"

One by one, Dorothy, LaVonne, Neil, and Delbert filed into the room as Sarah's eyes lit up.

"Oh my! Oh, my dear babies!" Sarah began to tear up. "Oh, you have no idea how wonderful it is to see you! I wish I could get up and wrap my arms around each one of you!"

"It's good to see you, too, old woman!" Neil grinned.

"You look good, Mom." Delbert smiled. "I wish I could give you a big ole kiss right on the cheek!"

"Oh, you lovely ladies! It's so good to see you! Are you keeping these boys of mine in line?"

"Well it's a tough job, you know!" Dorothy joked, winking at Delbert.

"I've got Neil trained already!" LaVonne giggled.

"And you all made that long drive just to come up and see me?" Sarah beamed.

"You bet, Mom. It's been way too long. How's the food in this joint?" Delbert smiled.

"Oh, ha ha, you know, it's really good." Sarah laughed. "It's not like home cooking but I like it just fine. They feed me a lot here. It sounds kinda funny to say that. But it's true. They tell me it's important to feed the body's ability to heal itself. They call it… hmm… I have trouble with the term… it's something like calorie input."

Sarah folded her hands over her belly, pleased with herself for coming close to the proper term.

As everyone visited, Dorothy and LaVonne looked around the small room. The lone window, across from Sarah's bed, looked out to various other buildings surrounding the hospital. No flowers or plants adorned the room, and only one chair sat in the corner. A constant quiet whooshing sound permeated the room as the ventilation system moved the air like the nurse described.

"So let me see these rings my boys bought for you girls!" Sarah said, wiping another tear from her eyes.

LaVonne and Dorothy quit looking around the room and walked closer to Sarah's bed as they removed their gloves. Sarah gingerly leaned closer to the edge of the bed to get a better view.

"Oh my, those look lovely, girls! So have you all set dates yet?" Sarah smiled, shifting back to her original spot in bed.

"Well, Delbert and I plan to get married in Springfield later this month, on the 29th!" Dorothy beamed.

"And Neil and I are looking at August 12!" LaVonne added.

"Oh, that just warms my heart," Sarah beamed for a moment then the joy disappeared from her eyes. "Kids, I can't tell you how much I wish I was out of here. I know they are doing me good and they are all very nice. But I sure miss all of you and getting to do things on my own."

"We know, sweetie, and we miss you, too," Dorothy reassured.

"Neil, honey," Sarah turned to Neil, "How are you doing? Are you still having those awful nightmares?"

"I'm doing okay, Mama," Neil glanced at Delbert as he answered, "I still have them from time to time, but I'm doing okay. Don't you worry."

"Well… I gotta admit, son, I have them too. I think about it a lot. The Fire… your dad… Dewey…"

No one said anything for a moment as Sarah was momentarily lost in her thoughts.

After several seconds, Delbert cleared his throat, which brought Sarah back to the present.

"And you both are working? Your jobs are going well?"

"Yes, Mama. We're both working and doing fine." Delbert stepped forward. "I've got a good job at a gas station."

"And I got on at the new Lily Tulip plant in town, working in the maintenance department. It's night shift but you know, it's a good job. Good pay." Neil grinned.

"Dorothy, how is your mother? Mrs. Moody was such a comfort to me when she visited while I was at St. John's."

"Mother is doing fine." Dorothy nodded. "I'll tell her you said hello. She's taking it easy now that tax season is over with!"

"Oh yes! I forgot about her accounting business."

Everyone smiled then the room grew quiet as they all ran out of things to say.

"I wish there were more chairs in here for all of you." Sarah sighed, looking around the room.

"It's okay, Mom. We know we can't stay long anyway," Delbert reassured Sarah.

"All this makes me appreciate the way things were at St. John's for sure. I didn't have to be so careful, and you all didn't have to wear special clothes. You could pretty much stay as long as you liked there."

"Yeah, we spent a lot of time getting to know each other, didn't we, Mom." Dorothy winked and smiled.

"Yes, dear, we sure did. And I like the sound of you calling me Mom."

Just then the door opened and an aide brought in Sarah's lunch, followed by a nurse.

"Holy smokes, it's chow time!" Neil said.

"Yes indeed!" the nurse chimed in. "Miss Sarah, are you ready for some lunch?"

"Oh my yes, I had lost track of time." Sarah gingerly shifted in her bed.

The nurse turned to the visitors.

"I'm afraid at this point you'll have to leave for a while. We will be checking Sarah's dressings and preparing for this afternoon's treatments."

"We understand. Mom, we're going to head out and see if we can scrounge up some lunch," Delbert hollered over the flurry of activity. "We'll come back and check on you after while."

"Ok, dear." Sarah grimaced as she shifted further in her bed while the aide raised it so she could eat.

"Let's go," Neil whispered, and the four filed out of the room.

After filling their bellies at a local café, they went back to the hospital and dropped by the gift shop.

"We've got to get her something. They apparently don't allow flowers up there since they are so concerned about germs," Dorothy said, looking around the shop.

Delbert and Neil rifled through the stuffed animals while Dorothy and LaVonne looked around.

"I think she needs this stuffed monkey awfully badly." Neil grinned as he held up the small toy.

"No, let's grab this one," Delbert said, reaching for a small stuffed bear. "That old stuffed bear that we all used to play with burned up in the fire. You know, it was originally hers when she was a girl. Maybe she'd like to have one again."

"Good idea." Neil grinned as the two walked triumphantly to the checkout counter. Dorothy and LaVonne shook their heads and laughed as they joined them.

Back up on the fifth floor, the four visitors checked in at the desk again to see if they could visit one more time.

"Oh, I'm sorry, she's going through her afternoon water bath still, then will have to lie for a while to dry," the nurse said after checking her chart. "Then we will have a debridement, so she will be away from her room for at least another hour, and will return fairly uncomfortable."

The four looked at each other and scowled.

"Well, could you please get this to her, and let her know it was from us?" Delbert asked. "Sounds like she's not going to be up to company, so we will just be on our way back home."

Later that afternoon, when Sarah carefully, painfully settled back into her bed, the nurse brought her the stuffed bear.

"Miss Sarah, while you were in your procedures, your visitors dropped by again and asked us to give you this when you came back to your room."

Sarah took the bear, which now smelled of disinfectant, and held it close to her.

"Oh, those sweet kids. They all used to play with the bear I still had from my childhood. It was lost in The Fire. They must have been thinking about that when they picked this out."

A single tear ran down Sarah's cheek.

"I'll let you rest now till dinner, Miss Sarah," the nurse said, slipping out of the room.

"Okay, thank you, dear," Sarah said, her eyelids drooping as she grew more fatigued from the busy afternoon.

An hour later, when she woke up from a nap, she was still holding the little stuffed bear in her arms.

July 18, 3:25p.m.
Pauline and Stanley Brooke's home, Roswell, NM

"Are you ready for this, kiddo?" Pauline asked as she adjusted Virginia's hat.

"I think so."

"Well, honey, you need to be sure. This needs to be what you want."

"Yes… yes it's what I want. All I've ever wanted was to be a wife and mother, to have someone who loves me and little babies to care for. It was all so wonderful with Dewey and Gary. I want that back."

Pauline didn't say anything.

"I know you think it's too soon, sis. You've said it before."

"Well, Virginia... it's not even been a year since... since everything happened." Pauline was trying to be careful with her words.

"I know... I... I know." Virginia leaned into the mirror to check her makeup.

After a few moments of silence, Virginia turned around to face her sister, a slight hint of a tear in her eyes.

"How do I look?" Virginia forced herself to smile.

"You look beautiful."

"Thank you. Let's do this."

The sisters opened the bedroom door and walked down the hall to the living room. Billy, standing by the front window, shifted his weight from one foot to the other while Stanley visited with Reverend Williamson nearby. The two men stopped talking and turned when Virginia walked into the room, followed by Pauline.

"And there's the bride!" the preacher proclaimed as he walked over toward Billy, "Shall we begin?"

Virginia stepped over next to Billy while Stanley walked to Pauline and reached for her hand. She grabbed him and let out a quiet sigh.

"It's going to be okay, dear," Stanley whispered, gently squeezing her hand.

Billy and Virginia stood nervously together as the preacher began to speak.

"Dearly beloved, we are gathered here today..."

"Neither of them are smiling," Pauline whispered to Stanley.

24

July 18, 1960, 12:10 p.m.
Neil and LaVonne Ritter's house, Springfield, Missouri

"Dewey!"

Neil's eyes popped open.

Where is he? I gotta get to him? Where... where are you? Where... where am I?

Drenched in sweat, Neil's head spun from side to side, wildly looking for Dewey through the smoke that wasn't there.

Neil screamed as LaVonne grabbed him.

"Neil! Neil, wake up! Neil, it's ok, you're home, in your bed!" she pleaded, gently shaking him, trying to bring him back to reality.

Neil turned and looked at LaVonne as he began to calm down.

LaVonne. LaVonne. Okay. Dewey's not here. I'm not on fire...

"It was just a nightmare, honey. It's alright," LaVonne ran her fingers through Neil's hair, wet with sweat.

Neil let out a long, heavy sigh.

"My God, LaVonne, am I going crazy?" Neil whispered, nearly in tears.

"No, honey. You're not crazy." LaVonne turned Neil toward her. "But we gotta do something to get you some relief. We gotta end these nightmares."

"Yeah, that would be nice." Neil gazed up at the ceiling. "It would be nice to be free of this, free of these memories. I can remember it all, just like it was yesterday."

"I know, love." LaVonne ran her hand over Neil's back. "We'll get you some help. Someone who can make all of this more bearable."

Neil sat quietly for a moment then a slight grin came across his face.

"What are you grinning about?" LaVonne asked.

"Oh, I just thought of something." Neil smiled.

"What is it, Neil?"

"I was just thinking… someday I want the month of October to be something more than misery for me. And I think I know what I want to do."

"What, love?"

"I want to make Halloween a big deal."

1:05 p.m.
University Hospital, Columbia, Missouri

"Was something wrong with the food today?"

The nurse's brow furrowed as she looked over Sarah's lunch tray. Everything was half-eaten.

"No, dear, I just wasn't very hungry."

"Well, Miss Sarah, you know we have to keep your calorie count pretty high to help you heal. So it's important that you eat."

"I know, I know." Sarah sighed. "I know it's here to help me. And I appreciate everything that everyone is doing. I just don't have my heart in it right now."

The nurse sat down on the edge of the bed, facing Sarah.

"Do you need to talk? You seem pretty down."

Sarah looked at her and cracked a weak smile.

"I'll be alright, dear."

Sarah looked away and closed her eyes.

The nurse got up, picked up the tray of half-eaten food, and walked out the door. As she left, she couldn't see the single tear running down Sarah's face.

The next day, when the nurse came in after lunch, Sarah hadn't touched any of her food. Without saying a word, she moved one of the chairs and sat down next to the bed.

"Miss Sarah, talk to me. What's going on? You didn't eat much yesterday, and you haven't touched your food today."

Sarah turned and looked at her then suddenly burst into tears.

"Oh, honey!" the nurse exclaimed as she leaned forward and carefully wrapped her arms around Sarah.

"Talk to me, Miss Sarah. What's wrong?"

Sarah pulled away, wiping her eyes.

"Oh, dear, I haven't wanted to say anything, but I'm just so sad. I miss my Orville so badly. I miss Dewey and Gary and Virginia, and all my kids. It's been nearly nine months since The Fire. Nine months since my husband held my hand… since… since he kissed me. Orville and I were very close. He was my one and only love. He was a very good man, a… a… a very loving man. He could be so gentle, and yet so tough. Such a hard worker. I swear my own daddy never worked as hard as Orville. Oh, Cindy, I'd give anything to feel his arms wrapped around me again."

The nurse smiled at her as she reached out to hold Sarah's face.

"And my son Dewey and little grandson Gary. It hurts *so bad* to remember losing them in The Fire. We could hear Dewey screaming as he died. We never heard anything out of little Gary. We didn't know he was dead. We thought maybe he was with his momma down in the bushes. But he was gone too."

"That's so awful, Miss Sarah. I can't imagine what you've been through."

Sarah looked down.

"I miss my kids. I miss my home. I don't even have a home anymore. I don't have any clothes. Nothing! And I know you all are doing good work to heal me. But it hurts so much. I'm sorry, I… I don't mean to be a… a crybaby. It just all has caught up with me and I'm just down. Just an old lady that's way down."

The nurse lifted Sarah's head to make eye contact.

"Miss Sarah, I'm so sorry you're hurting. We all love you here, and we know this is a tough fight for you. We don't want you to be so down. I'm so sorry about Orville and Dewey and Gary. Sweetie, I can't imagine how you feel. But please know that we are all here for you. We love you and will be happy to listen any time you want to talk. Okay?"

Sarah smiled weakly.

"Thank you, dear. I appreciate all of you, and I don't mean to bellyache like this... I don't mean to sound ungrateful. It all gets to be too much sometimes. These burns hurt on the outside, but they are nothing compared to how badly it hurts inside."

"Oh, Miss Sarah…" The nurse leaned forward and held Sarah for a long time.

4:18 p.m., July 20, 1960
Norman Ritter's house, Springfield, Missouri

Jerry jumped when the phone rang. The loud ringing started just as she began lowering a chicken into boiling water for the evening meal, and she nearly dropped it.

"Hang on, hang on," she hollered, quickly washing her hands then darting over to answer the phone on the eighth ring.

"Hello?"

"Mrs. Ritter?"

"Yes, who's this?"

"Mrs. Ritter, my name is Alice Comstock. I'm the patient social services coordinator here at the University Hospital in Columbia. Would Mr. Ritter happen to be around?"

"Yes, just a moment."

Jerry set down the phone and ran out to the garage where Norman was busily working on his son Dennis' bicycle.

"Dear, it's a lady from the hospital in Columbia. She says she'd like to talk to you."

"Is something wrong with Mom?" Norman asked through his cigarette.

"She didn't say." Jerry shook her head. "She just asked to talk with you."

With a sigh, Norman stood up and grabbed a rag to wipe the grease from his hands.

"Let me wash up real quick. Tell her I'll be right there."

Within thirty seconds, Norman picked up the phone.

"Hello, this is Norman Ritter."

"Hello, Mr. Ritter. I'm sorry to bother you. My name is Alice Comstock, and I'm the patient social services coordinator here at the hospital in Columbia. I believe your mother is one of our patients here?"

"Yes, that's right. My mother is Sarah Ritter. Is she okay, Mrs.

Comstock?"

"Well, Mr. Ritter…"

"Please call me Norman."

"Well, Norman, the answer is yes and no. Her skin grafts are doing well at this point. However a problem has developed."

Norman scowled.

"What kind of problem?"

"Our nurses have noticed that she is not eating much. That's troubling because we have to keep her on a high caloric intake to give the body enough energy to heal. But even more troubling is the fact that this lack of appetite is caused by depression."

"Depression?"

"Yes, sir. Your mother has cried to our nurses on more than one occasion. According to my notes, it appears that much of the traumatic events from the night of the fire are catching up with her. She misses your father, and the son who died, I believe his name was Dewey?"

"Yes, that's correct."

"And she's upset that she doesn't have any clothes, no home. And she misses all of you very badly."

"Bless her heart," Norman sighed, "I feel bad because I haven't been up there in a few of months. But I know a couple of my brothers went up with their fiancés earlier this month."

"Yes, sir. I understand, and I know it's a bit of a drive for all of you to come up here. But we are very concerned about this depression, and we believe we need to give her a change of scenery very soon or else her healing may begin to diminish. That would not be good."

"I agree ma'am. What do we need to do? What kind of change of scenery are you suggesting?"

"Well, Norman, something that we have to do from time to time, especially for patients needing longer-term attention, is we furlough them. We temporarily release them to the family, so that they can stay with relatives in hopes that it would raise their spirits and bring them out of their depression. Is there someone she could stay with?"

"I'm sure we could figure out somewhere for her. With eight kids, surely we can come up with something. How long do you recommend this furlough last?"

"With the degree of depression that we are observing, we'd really like to see her have a long-term visit. I recommend four or five weeks. Then after that time period, she will return to continue her treatments. Then we will look to schedule another furlough through Thanksgiving and Christmas. Considering how depressed she has been, we do not believe she should be here, removed from family, during the holidays."

"Well, Mrs. Comstock, I'm sure we can make that happen. Whether we park her at one home or move her around, I'm sure we can take care of her."

"That's wonderful, Mr. Ritter. I do need to note that while she is staying with someone, her wounds will require considerable care, and her bedsheets will need to be cleaned daily, to prevent infection. We will send instructions along for her daily care."

"That shouldn't be a problem, ma'am. Do you have a date in mind for us to pick her up?"

"Yes, Mr. Ritter, I'd really like to see this furlough start on August 5th. That's a Friday. Do you think someone could be here to pick her up and get her started on this little reprieve?"

"Absolutely. I'm off work on most Fridays so I can drive up to get her. What time do you need me there?"

"I'd suggest you get here around 11:00 if possible. There will be some paperwork to sign and instructions to hand over to you before you leave with her."

"Okay that sounds good. Thank you, Mrs. Comstock. I appreciate everything you people are doing for her. I'll see you on the 5th around 11:00."

11:13 a.m., August 5
Columbia, Missouri

Sarah sat nervously on the side of her bed, hands folded in her lap, looking at the clock on the wall across the room.

"Come on, Norman. Come get your mama. Get me outta here for a while," she muttered under her breath.

A quiet knock at the door interrupted Sarah letting out a long sigh, as Jerry peeked her head in the door.

"Mom?" Jerry called out softly.

Sarah's eyes lit up.

"Oh, honey!"

Jerry stepped over and leaned over, carefully hugging as Sarah wrapped her arms around her and held on tight.

"Oh, I've missed you, dear," Sarah sniffed, "I'm so excited to get out of here for a while."

"We're so happy to see you. I'm sorry we haven't made it up here more often."

"Don't worry about it. The important thing is that you are here now, and we're gonna get me outta here."

"You betcha, sweetie. Are you ready to go?"

"Honey, I was ready two days ago," Sarah snorted.

The two women chuckled as Jerry picked up a bag that she'd set down to hug Sarah.

"We brought you some going-home clothes!" Jerry beamed, holding up a nightgown for Sarah.

"Oh, Jerry!" Sarah smiled as she reached out to touch the soft fabric. "All I'm used to wearing is hospital gowns. That is so pretty! Thank you, love."

As Jerry slowly helped Sarah out of her hospital gown, she noticed the large bandages on Sarah's shoulders, arms, and legs.

"Take your time getting into this new one, Mom. We don't want to hurt any of your… your places… as we do this."

"It's okay, dear. I just call them my burns."

After getting her pretty well covered, Jerry reached back down in the bag and brought out a pair of slippers.

"Oh boy, new slippers!" Sarah laughed. Jerry leaned over and slipped them on her feet. "Those are so soft!"

Just then. they heard a quiet knock on the door as Norman stuck his head in the room.

"Hey, you old bat!" Norman grinned.

"Hey there, big fella!" Sarah beamed as he walked over to her and carefully gave her a big hug. "Rumor has it you're gonna take me outta here."

"You bet, Mom. We're going to take you to Seymour, to stay with Speedy and Wanda," Norman grinned.

"Sounds great, son. Let's go."

"I've got all your gear," Norman said, holding up the bags of bandages, antiseptic and other supplies for keeping Sarah's wounds properly treated during her furlough.

With another knock on the door, an orderly showed up with a

wheelchair.

"Miss Sarah?" the orderly asked.

"Yes, dear!"

"I'm going to give you a ride to the front door to get you in these nice people's car."

"Thank you dear," Sarah sighed, settling down into the wheelchair.

"I'll go get the car," Norman said, stepping quickly out the door.

Once Norman brought the car to the entrance, Sarah was carefully loaded into the back seat on the passenger side. Jerry climbed in behind Norman and helped Sarah get comfortable. They brought extra pillows to make sure she was well cushioned.

"Are we ready, ladies?" Norman looked in the rear-view mirror.

"Ready, son," Sarah beamed from the back seat.

Within ten minutes, Sarah was sound asleep, her head leaning against one of the pillows.

25

August 5, 3:37p.m.
Wanda and Speedy Bollinger's House,
Seymour, Missouri

"Here we are!" Norman called out.

"This is Wanda and Speedy's place?"

Sarah sat up and looked around as Norman pulled into the driveway of the brick home on the southern outskirts of Seymour, Missouri.

"Yep, this is the place!" Norman said, setting the brake. "They had just moved in to this house before the fire."

Sarah slowly moved in her seat while Jerry jumped out and opened her door.

"Here, Mom, let me help you. Take your time."

Sarah turned, wincing from the pain of her raw flesh under bandages, and swung her legs out the door. Norman stood behind Jerry, watching as he lit a cigarette.

"Well, you got that far, old woman!" Norman grinned. "Doing pretty good, I'd say!"

Suddenly the front door of the house flew open and Wanda came trotting down the steps with Speedy taking his time behind her.

"Hey, Mom!" Wanda stepped quickly to the car to help Jerry steady Sarah as she slowly leaned out of the car to stand up.

"Looks like y'all survived the trip down!" Speedy joked, shaking Norman's hand and patting him on the back, "Did ya have any trouble?"

"Not a bit," Norman said as he took the cigarette out of his mouth. "Mom slept most of the way. We had some extra pillows in back to try to keep her comfortable."

"That son of mine is a pretty good driver." Sarah tried to smile through the grimaces as she began to move forward, working the stiffness out of her joints after the long ride. With Jerry and Wanda carefully holding her arms, she walked up to Norman and Speedy.

"It was a nice ride, what little I was awake for. Thank you, son."

She pulled Norman's arm and he bent over and kissed her on the cheek. She then moved over to Speedy, who leaned down and instinctively began to wrap his arm around her.

"Careful where you touch her, Speedy. Those skin grafts are pretty fresh and she's tender," Norman called out.

With a quick jerk, he pulled his arm back. Sarah leaned in and kissed him on the cheek, patting him on the arm.

"Good to see you, Speedy. Sure is a nice-looking place you got here."

"Thanks, Mom. We're pretty happy with it," Speedy said as everyone turned to get Sarah up the steps and into the house.

Moving slowly, she made it to the front porch while Speedy held the door open. Norman followed behind Wanda and Jerry, busily keeping Sarah steady as she stepped into the living room.

"Oh, Wanda, this is soooooo nice!"

"We sure like it. Here, Mom, let's get you over to the couch."

The couch was set up with extra pillows and a sheet. Positioned against the north wall, it offered a good view out the picture window on the east wall. Jerry and Wanda helped Sarah carefully lower herself to the couch.

"Oh, thank you, girls. I'm sorry to be so much trouble," Sarah sighed as she kicked off the house shoes that Norman and Jerry brought her.

"You're no trouble at all," Jerry reassured her as everyone began to settle into chairs around the room.

"Are you hurting, Mom?" Wanda asked.

"Yes, dear," Sarah sighed, "Hurting pretty bad. I think I'm ready for some aspirin."

9:15 p.m.

"I'm trying to be careful, Mom."

Wanda grimaced as she gently pulled the first bandage off of the back of Sarah's thigh.

"You're doing fine, dear. It just hurts," Sarah grunted, gritting her teeth. "It's just part of my world now. Gotta do this."

Sarah lay face-down, naked on the bed in the spare room at the end of the hall. Following the hospital's orders, her dressings were to be changed twice a day to prevent infection. Large gauze bandages covered the places on the backs of her thighs and buttocks where the skin was harvested for her grafts. Her worst burns, on her left shoulder, arm, and leg, were the graft sites and also required fresh dressings. All the other burns, which dotted her body, were in various stages of healing and required no bandaging despite remaining tender to the touch.

"I'm looking forward to the day when all this quits hurting so much," Sarah sighed as Wanda gingerly applied a new bandage.

"Have the doctors said anything about that, about when things are going to start getting better?"

"It's going to be a while. They tell me burns like this take a while to heal, maybe over a year. But, Wanda, I'm here to tell you, this is nothing compared to what some of those patients there are going through there at that hospital. It could have been much worse. I keep reminding myself of that. It could have been much worse."

"Very true, Mom." Wanda nodded as she began to remove the next bandage.

"Your poor dad." Sarah sighed. "I'd hate to think of how he would have suffered if he would have lived. I just can't imagine how badly he was burned."

Wanda didn't say anything. She knew her mother didn't realize that she was burned far worse than Orville.

"Oh, Orville, if you'd just jumped…" Sarah sniffed.

3:40 p.m.
Marriage License Office, Greene County Courthouse, Springfield, Missouri

Neil shifted nervously as LaVonne rested her arms on the counter. In a bright yellow sleeveless dress with matching heels, she glanced at Neil, who was dressed in black slacks and a white shirt, both of which seemed to hang loosely on his thin frame.

He needs to eat… and sleep.

The clerk behind the counter methodically pulled a form out of the big filing cabinet and brought it over to the counter.

"Both of you need to fill this out," she said without looking up, "and I'll need some identification."

LaVonne dug into her little yellow purse for her driver's license as Neil pulled his out of his wallet.

The clerk grabbed the licenses and turned to begin entering the information in her ledger. She stopped and looked at Neil's license, then turned to finally look at them.

"Mr. Ritter, you're not twenty-one," she declared, looking over her glasses.

"Yes, ma'am, that's correct."

"You're going to need a parent's signature. Since you're underage, it's required. Get your mom or dad to sign the form. Gotta have their signature before we can process the license."

Neil looked at LaVonne.

"It's okay, Neil." LaVonne turned, resting her hand on Neil's arm. "Let's see if one of the twins will drive us to Seymour tomorrow to get your mom's signature."

The clerk set the licenses back on the counter.

"Just bring that form back when you've got the signature and we'll get it processed."

"Thank you, we will."

The next day, Delmas and Mary drove them to Wanda and Speedy's house in Seymour, where Sarah happily signed the form. The following Friday, August 12, Neil and LaVonne were married at the home of Reverend Spindler, the same preacher who performed Delmas and Mary's wedding in Sarah's hospital room, as well as the triple funeral in Ava. Norman and Jerry, LaVonne's parents Robert and Edna Kile, and Mrs. Spindler served as witnesses.

7:10 p.m. August 13
Billy and Virginia McCormack's House, Roswell, NM

Virginia sat on the steps of the little porch outside their house, taking an occasional sip of tea, hoping to calm her nerves and the nausea in her stomach. She quickly stood up when Billy Joe's noisy pickup pulled into the driveway. Straightening her dress, she walked over as Billy shut off the truck and clamored out.

Billy Joe looked at her and frowned.

"What's up, baby? Where's that smile? Are you okay?"

Virginia leaned up to kiss him as Billy Joe leaned down.

"I'm pregnant."

26

4:22am, September 8
Speedy and Wanda Bollinger's House,
Seymour, Missouri

Wanda crawled back into bed after throwing up for the third time in two hours.

"Speedy?" Wanda shoved her husband to wake him up. He responded with a snort.

"Speedy, wake up." Wanda shoved him again.

After a couple of hard snorts and a few quick blinks, Speedy woke up.

"What'sa matter, Wanda?"

"Honey, I think we are going to have to get some help to get Mom back up to Columbia. I'm just too sick."

"You been throwin' up again?"

"Yes." Wanda sighed. "I'm just miserable."

"Okay," Speedy grunted as he threw the covers back to get out of bed. "I'll call Paul Triplett over at the funeral home to see if he's got an ambulance available to take her back."

Similar to Clarence Clinkingbeard's operation in Ava, the Bergman-Miller Funeral Home in Seymour had cars that doubled as hearses or ambulances. As a trusted family friend, the Bollingers knew Paul Triplett would take good care of Sarah and get her back to Columbia safely.

7:30am, September 9

Wanda and Sarah sat across the living room from each other. Wanda sipped her coffee as she watched Sarah stir a spoon around in her tea. Someone a few houses away fired up a lawnmower. The horn of the 7:30 eastbound freight train blew several times as it rocketed through the other side of town. Birds chirped and flitted about, eating from the feeder perched just outside the open window. Sarah continued to stir her tea.

"Mom?"

No answer.

"Mom?"

Still no answer.

"Mother?"

Wanda never called Sarah "mother." The change in wording brought her back. Sarah looked up.

"Mom, you haven't touched your tea. What's on your mind?"

"Sorry, dear. I was lost in my own thoughts."

Wanda kept looking at her.

"I… I guess I was just sitting here thinking about how I'm looking forward to getting back up there and continuing to heal up… but part of me wants to stay right here and not have to go through that any more up there…"

Sarah finally took a sip of her tea.

"And?"

"And another part of me just wants to go back. Back to Ava. Back to the farm. Back to that drafty old house… Your father would have turned 63 just a couple of months ago. I miss him."

"I know, Mom. We all miss him…"

Sarah and Wanda finally made eye contact. Wanda set her coffee down, walked over and kneeled in front of Sarah, gently laying her hands on Sarah's legs, careful to avoid her burns.

"Momma, you gotta keep living. You gotta keep going, for them. For Daddy and Dewey and Gary. There's going to be more grandkids, and they'll need you. All of us, we need you. You gotta be strong, be tough. You can do this, and you've got all of us cheering you on. We can't be there all the time like we were at St.

John's, but… but we're still there for you. And this will be a short stay, just a couple of months, and then you can come back and we will all enjoy the holidays together."

Sarah's eyes welled up with tears.

"Thank you, dear. I promise I'll be strong. And you're right, I'll get through this. It'll be nice to be with someone for the holidays."

Wanda got up and gave her mom a gentle hug.

"Jerry should be here any time, and we are going to ride up with you to get you settled back in at Columbia."

"Are you sure, Wanda? You've been awfully sick the last couple of days."

"I'm feeling better today, Mom. Should be just fine. Just remember, we will be back up in November to get you again, so that you can be down here with all of us at Thanksgiving and Christmastime."

"That'll be nice for sure."

Two days later, as Sarah settled back into her routine in Columbia, Wanda went to the doctor in Springfield and found out why she had been so sick; she was six weeks pregnant.

27

October 27, 1960 - 2:00a.m.
University Hospital, Columbia, Missouri

As Sarah lay sleeping, quietly snoring, her left hand began to twitch. Her brow furrowed. Her right leg jerked.

The house is on fire! Oh my God, it's hot! I don't want to jump! Orville jump with me! Neil catch me! Neil!

Rachel Hobson, the nurse on overnight duty, was enjoying the quiet when she suddenly heard a loud thud down the hall, followed by cries for help. She jumped up and ran down the hall toward the cries. Turning into the room, she saw Sarah, out of her bed, lying on the floor and sobbing uncontrollably.

"Oh my God, Miss Sarah! What happened?" she tried to whisper to keep from frightening the other patients on the floor.

"Where am I?" Sarah looked around, trying to get her bearings.

"Honey, you're in Columbia. At the hospital. We are treating you for your burns."

"Oh. Oh. Oh my." Sarah turned to look at Rachel. "I was back in that house. We were all burning. I had to jump."

2:00a.m.
Billy and Virginia McCormack's home, Roswell, NM

As Virginia lay sleeping, her body began to twitch.

The house is on fire! Oh my God, it's hot! I don't want to jump! Dewey, I'm scared! Dewey!

"Dewey!" Virginia screamed as she sat up in bed.

Billy, startled out of a deep sleep, jumped up out of bed, and fumbled for the light, expecting to find someone in their room. He turned and saw Virginia, drenched in sweat, screaming for Dewey. He reached down and grabbed her arms, shaking her.

"Virginia! Virginia, wake up! Virginia!"

"Oh God, Dewey!" Virginia crumpled into Billy's arms.

2:00a.m.
Neil and LaVonne Ritter's house, Springfield, Missouri

As Neil lay sleeping, quietly snoring, his body began to twitch.

Dewey! I can't get to you! Dewey!

"Dewey!" Neil screamed.

LaVonne shook him till he quit screaming.

"Neil, it's okay, love. Dewey's not here. You're okay. You're not in that house. It's all okay, Neil."

With wild eyes and drenched in sweat, he looked around. Standing in the hallway, with LaVonne's arms around him, he was nearly hyperventilating.

6:10 p.m.
Billy and Virginia McCormack's home, Roswell, NM

Billy and Virginia sat in silence across the tiny table from each other. Virginia, with her head down, swirled her fork around in the stroganoff on her plate, occasionally taking a small bite, but mostly swirling her fork. Billy sat watching her.

"Virginia?"

No answer.

"Virginia?"

Still no answer.

"Virginia, look at me."

When Virginia looked up, Billy saw tears in her eyes. He scowled.

"I suppose this… this *mood* you are in, it has to do with those dirt poor farmer backwoods hillbillies back in Missouri, doesn't it!"

Virginia lowered her head again.

"Answer me!" Billy yelled, pounding his fist on the table, sending food and dishes into the air.

Virginia, her eyes wide, looked up quickly after Billy's outburst.

"They were not hillbillies! And they were sweet people!" Virginia's voice cracked as she began to tremble.

"This is so stupid! It was a whole year ago! Your precious Dewey is dead! Do you hear me? He's dead! And so is that little boy! You're my wife now, not his! You're pregnant with our baby, not his! So move on! I don't want to hear about precious Dewey ever again! Do you hear me?"

"Oh my God, I can't believe you just said that! How could you say that, Billy? You heartless monster!"

Virginia threw down her fork, jumped up and ran crying into their bedroom, slamming the door behind her.

Billy sat at the table, still clenching his fists, trying to calm down. After several minutes of expecting Virginia to come back to the table, he got up and let out a sigh.

"I can't believe I have to go apologize for saying something bad about her precious dead guy," he muttered, walking toward the bedroom door.

6:10p.m.
Neil Ritter Residence, Springfield, Missouri

Neil and LaVonne sat in silence across the tiny table from each other. Neil, with his head down, swirled his fork around in the spaghetti on his plate, occasionally taking a small bite, but mostly swirling his fork. LaVonne sat watching him.

"Neil?"

No answer.

"Neil?"

Still no answer.

"Neil, look at me."

Neil looked up, tears in his eyes.

"Neil, honey, talk to me."

"I… I don't know if I can…"

"Try."

"It's… It's been… It was a year ago. A year ago this morning. Dad, Dewey, little Gary, they've been gone a year."

"Yeah," LaVonne answered, "I've been thinking about that date coming up."

"Yeah, me, too." Neil lowered his head again. "It's been bothering me… really bad."

"How can I help you, honey? Tell me what I can do."

"Nothing really. I just…"

LaVonne waited for him to finish his thought.

Neil took a deep breath.

"It may sound silly, but… but it's how I feel. I just… I just want to… to be able to smile again in October. You know what I mean? I feel like it's all just so… so sad. After all this time, I still regret not being able to… to save Dewey. It hurts. I don't know if I'll ever get over it. I wish I could just get rid of the memories of that night. But…"

Neil looked up again at LaVonne.

"I want to find a way to be happy again."

28

As planned, Sarah was furloughed from Columbia in November, so that she could enjoy the holidays with family. She spent several weeks at Norman's house, with Jerry taking on the daily duties to clean her wounds. Just after Christmas, Sarah moved in with Neil and LaVonne.

January 9, 1961, 8:12p.m.
Neil and LaVonne Ritter's house

LaVonne took a deep breath then gently knocked on the door as she opened it into the darkened room.

"Mom?" she whispered, looking through the shadows toward Sarah's bed. "Mom, are you awake?"

"I'm awake, dear." Sarah's voice trembled.

"Are you okay, Mom? What's wrong?" LaVonne fumbled through the dark to find the small lamp on the nightstand.

"Oh, honey, this old woman is just thinking too much. Remembering too much."

Sarah squinted when LaVonne turned on the light then sat down on the bed beside her.

"Anything you need to talk about?"

"No." Sarah smiled and patted LaVonne's leg. "I was just thinking about Orville again."

LaVonne grabbed Sarah's hand and gave it a gentle squeeze. Sarah wiped a tear from her eye.

"I'm guessing it's time again, isn't it?" Sarah sighed after a brief silence.

"Yes, it is," LaVonne said softly, "I've already run you a nice warm bath. You can enjoy soaking for a while before we begin."

"Okay, dear. I'll try to be stronger for you this time." Sarah grimaced, struggling to sit up.

LaVonne gently grabbed her arm and helped her steady herself on the side of the bed.

"I swear, LaVonne, the backs of my thighs and my backside where they took the skin for those grafts hurt far worse than the burns at this point. It's hard to get comfy when you feel like you've been under a filet knife."

"I can only imagine how that feels. I'm so sorry." LaVonne grunted, helping Sarah to her feet.

The two walked slowly together, LaVonne following while Sarah shuffled across the hall into the bathroom.

"I'm going to help you get in the tub," LaVonne directed, helping Sarah out of her nightgown.

"I appreciate that, as always."

"Let me get those old dressings off before you get in."

LaVonne knelt down and carefully pulled the dressings off Sarah wounds. The gauze pads were oversized so that the tape remained at least two inches away from her many tender spots. Removing each pad, LaVonne looked over Sarah's grafted sections on her shoulder, arms, and legs. The skin that had been harvested from Sarah's buttocks and thighs continued to show signs of growth and healing, a wonderful improvement over the horrifying burns that a year earlier terrified anyone who saw them. But the burns still looked awful, and she tried to not look too long. She knew closer inspection was coming in a little while.

The raw sections of Sarah's flesh where the harvests took place showed signs of improvement as well but still looked painful and deep, and had much healing left to do.

LaVonne helped Sarah step gingerly into the tub.

"How's the water temperature, Mom?"

"It's fine, dear," Sarah sighed as she settled in to the deep tub, the water enveloping her body.

LaVonne slipped a rolled-up towel under Sarah's neck as she settled against the back of the tub.

"That feels really good." Sarah looked up and smiled.

"I'm glad. I'm going to let you lay here and soak for fifteen minutes, then I'll be back."

"Then the bad stuff comes."

LaVonne looked down at the floor.

"Yes, honey." LaVonne looked back up at Sarah. "I'm afraid we have to. To prevent infection."

"I know." Sarah smiled weakly. "I just hate it. It hurts so bad."

"I know. I'll be back."

LaVonne closed the door and just stood there for a moment.

Dear God, give me strength. I hate to put her through this yet again.

Taking a deep breath, LaVonne walked to kitchen to the pot of boiling water on the stove. Using the tongs on the counter, she pulled out the five surgical knives that she started heating before getting Sarah into the bath. Laying them on a clean dish towel, she set the tongs down and stared at the knives.

One knife for each major wound. Don't use the same knife for more than one wound. Cut away all the dead skin and be on the lookout for infection.

The doctor's instructions replayed in her mind as she stared at the knives. She turned and set a timer for fifteen minutes.

8:29p.m.

Sarah bit her lip as LaVonne leaned over with the first knife to work on the shoulder wound. Trying to keep from trembling, LaVonne brought the tip of the knife to Sarah's skin.

Here we go... again...

Sarah let out a brief shriek as LaVonne began to cut away at the scabbed area.

"You okay?" LaVonne asked without looking up.

"Yes."

Still in the water, which was now starting to cool, Sarah held her breath while LaVonne worked, releasing little sections of bloody scabs and skin into the water.

"Honey, I'm trying to be tough," Sarah whispered breathlessly.

"I know, Mom. You're doing fine. I don't mean to hurt you." LaVonne fought back tears.

"I know. We have to do this. You, Wanda, and Jerry have worked so hard to help me. You know..."

LaVonne loosened a large section of dead skin, making Sarah yelp.

"Sorry, Mom, that was a big one." LaVonne sniffed.

"It's okay," Sarah continued, thinking past the pain, "You know this sounds awful, but... Jerry... when I stayed with her and Norman... she... she had to put a strainer in the tub drain. To... to catch all the bits of flesh so that it wouldn't clog her drain."

LaVonne stopped for a moment. The thought almost made her wretch. Collecting herself, she finally said quietly, "I didn't know that."

The process continued until the first wound, the large shoulder burn, was clean and free of dead skin. LaVonne then switched to a clean knife and moved to the one on Sarah's arm, where a large cinder had imbedded itself in her skin when she was at the back of the house, trying to get to Dewey.

"This is the deep one, Mom. We're going to tackle it next."

"Ok."

LaVonne began to scrape the wound as Sarah let out a yell.

"Oh God, honey, can we please leave that one alone?"

"No, Mom, I'm sorry. We have to do this. You don't want to get it infected."

"I know, but it just hurts so bad."

LaVonne continued to work as Sarah cried from the pain. Her cries turned to sobs. LaVonne worked deeper to get the last of the dead skin removed from the wound. After several minutes, the wound, now thoroughly cleaned, filled with blood as LaVonne swished water to carry it away.

"You're bleeding pretty good here, Mom. I've got to get it to stop or you'll develop a scab and we can't allow you to scab up."

The work continued as Sarah wiped her eyes and grimaced, while LaVonne scraped at the dead skin. When LaVonne moved down to the burn on the right leg, Sarah grabbed her arm, tears streaming down her face.

"Please, LaVonne, please! Can we just wait? Can we just not do that one? I don't know if I can take much more!"

LaVonne began to cry.

"Mom… I don't mean to hurt you. But… if we don't do this right, when you go back to Columbia, they… they might have to start over on some of this. And you don't want that, do you?"

Sarah pulled LaVonne close, and the two women held each other, crying, for several minutes. When Sarah finally loosened her grip, they remained face-to-face, forehead touching forehead.

"Mom, honey, I'm so sorry," LaVonne said between sniffles. "I want to do this right. We can't send you back to Columbia with your burns not properly cared for."

"I know, love. I know. You're doing what's right," Sarah whispered.

They held each other for a few more moments then LaVonne pulled away, wiping her eyes and nose.

"Let me wash my hands real quick," LaVonne said, getting up. "Gotta stay clean after all this blubbering."

"Somehow it felt good to get that out," Sarah sighed, wiping her eyes. "I needed to get those tears out, love."

"I understand. I think we both did." LaVonne knelt back down beside Sarah. "Let's get this finished up, before you catch a chill. That water is really cooling off."

After several minutes of scraping, LaVonne was finished. The bathtub, once clean but now filled with chunks of skin mixed with blood, stood as a stark reminder of how large her wounds were, and the amount of pain Sarah suffered with each cleaning.

LaVonne gently applied new dressings to every wound while Sarah sat quietly. Both of them heard the furnace kick on.

"Are you cold, Mom?"

"No, dear. That air movement from the furnace actually feels good on my skin. But I do look forward to putting some clothes on. This old woman isn't accustomed to laying around naked for so long."

LaVonne looked up and saw Sarah grinning. Breaking the tension with the comment, both women snickered. LaVonne shook her head.

"I sure know where Neil gets it. You're a mess!" LaVonne winked at Sarah.

"You know, Orville used to have to get after me," Sarah snickered, "With that many kids, when things got rowdy, I usually joined in the ruckus. Then when Orville would have enough, he'd look at me and say 'Sarah Elizabeth! If you'd settle down, these kids would!'"

Shaking her head, LaVonne reached over to the counter and unfolded a white sheet. To keep Sarah comfortably clothed after the daily scrapings, she covered her with a sheet that had a hole cut in it for Sarah's head to poke through. Wearing the sheet like a big poncho, Sarah could move freely about the house and not have to worry about getting any blood on the furniture where she sat. She walked into the living room and gingerly sat down on the couch, adjusting the pillows around her.

LaVonne walked into the kitchen.

"Mom, do you need anything before I start cleaning things up?"

"Some tea would be nice, if it wouldn't be too much trouble," Sarah called over to the kitchen.

"No trouble at all," LaVonne called back as she stood trembling, gripping the kitchen counter.

29

January 13, 9:05 a.m.
Neil and LaVonne Ritter's house

Sarah leaned forward on the couch, dressed in a loose-fitting gown and slippers. Facing her, LaVonne sat on a footstool, also leaning forward as the two ladies held hands and the tops of their heads rested against one another.

"LaVonne," Sarah said quietly, a slight tremble in her voice, "I know this has been tough on you, but I wanted to tell you how much I appreciate you taking such good care of me. You've scrubbed my burns, you've held me when I cried, you've listened to me talk on and on. I don't know how I'll ever thank you enough."

"I'm glad I got to do it," LaVonne whispered, "You're right, it's been tough. But I wanted to do it. And I'm glad we had the time, just the two of us."

"You and Jerry both did a wonderful job. It was so nice to be with family during Thanksgiving and Christmas. Makes me feel bad for the patients up there that didn't get to come home."

The two sat in silence for a few moments, still holding on to each other.

"You know, Mom," LaVonne finally broke the silence, "All our late-night conversations, all those things you told me, about that night, about the fire… I'll keep all that to myself."

"Thank you, dear. I appreciate that. And I appreciated you listening to me when I talked about it… I had to get it out."

"You're very welcome."

The two women fell quiet again. The only sound within the room was the clock on the end table ticking.

"I don't want to go back," Sarah whispered.

"I know. But if all goes well, you'll be out once and for all sometime around May. Then no more hospitals."

"Right."

Sarah let out a long sigh.

"I guess Mary is going to have her baby any time now," she said, trying to change the subject.

"She sure is." LaVonne smiled. "She's due any day. Last time I saw her she was pretty miserable."

"I hope it goes well. Promise me that you'll let me know what she has and when."

"Of course, Mom. I'll let you know."

Just then they heard the sound of a car pulling up in the driveway. The two women parted and LaVonne got up to look out the window.

"That's Delbert and Dorothy," LaVonne said, turning back to Sarah, "They're taking you back up to Columbia today."

"Okay, then." Sarah grunted as she got up from the couch. "Time to hit the indoor plumbing before that long car ride."

6:40 p.m.
Billy and Virginia McCormack's house,
Roswell, New Mexico

Virginia leaned heavily on the table as she leaned over to adjust the pillow before slowly sitting down on it to eat. Billy, not waiting for her return after she brought his plate, voraciously cut and chewed the remains of his pork chop as she settled in across from him.

"You're sure moving slow," he said with a mouth full of pork.

Everything hurts. I hope this isn't as rough as when Gary was born.

"I'm okay. Just a little uncomfortable…"

"You not eating?"

"I'm… I'm not really hungry."

"Well, this sure is good. You're missing out. Did you make

another pork chop?"

"Yes, I thought I might…"

"Bring it on in here, since you're not going to eat it."

Billy didn't look up as she winced, once again leaning on the table to get up to bring in the other pork chop, then sat down again to savor another sip of ice water.

"Billy, I need to talk to you about something."

"I'm listening."

"I… I'm concerned about this baby… about after it's born."

He kept eating without looking up.

"If I may, when my first child was born…"

Billy looked up and glared at her.

I'd better not say his name.

"When he was born, there were complications. For me and him. He required a lot of attention. And if this baby does, too, my sister isn't going to be able to help as much as we might need. I… I'm wondering if maybe we should move back to Missouri, to the town of Ozark, where my parents live. They could help take care of the baby and look after me if… if I'm having a hard time…"

Billy quit chewing and stared at her.

"So what about me?" he said, finally. "Am I just supposed to quit my job?"

"Well, Billy, all that big equipment that you run, you could get a job doing that back there, too. Ozark is just outside Springfield, which is a big city, nearly 100,000 people and growing all the time. And Ozark is growing, too. I know people need guys like you to run bulldozers and dump trucks and all those other big machines. I know you could find work."

Billy looked down, took another bite, then looked back up at her.

"Back to the hillbillies, huh?" he snickered.

"They're not hillbillies."

"We'll see." He shook his head. "Alright. We'll go. Back to Mommy and Daddy. Who knows, maybe they could fork over some money from time to time too."

Billy got up from the table, tossed his napkin on his plate, gave his chair a hard shove, and walked off.

Hopefully this will get better when the baby is born...

30

April 7, 1961 – 6:00p.m.
Norman Ritter's house, Springfield, Missouri

The entire room was silent. Norman sat at his normal spot, at the head of the table, pulled his cigarette papers and Prince Albert tobacco can out of his shirt pocket and set them on the table. Jerry, Dorothy, Mary, Barbara, LaVonne, and Wanda busied themselves cleaning plates and silverware off the table as Delmas, Delbert, Speedy, Neil, and Ray sat quietly and smoked. The only sound in the room was the clanking of dishes and an occasional word or two passed between the women.

Norman pulled out a paper and creased it between his index finger and thumb.

Jerry ran water over the dishes as Mary and Dorothy wiped each side of the table down, dancing around each man while they worked.

Delbert glanced across the table at Speedy and Ray, each looking back for a moment then shifting their glance to Delmas, who was watching Mary. Neil kept his eyes on Norman.

Noman popped the top of the can, then filled the paper to his liking with tobacco, set the can down, and slowly licked the edge of the paper.

Barbara dried plates as Jerry washed silverware.

Norman pulled out his lighter, lit his fresh cigarette, then set his lighter down.

Jerry laid down the last of the newly cleaned silverware then waved off Barbara as she reached for the stack to begin drying. All six ladies turned around to face the room full of silent men huddled around the table. They crossed their arms and leaned back against the counters at the same time.

Norman cleared his throat.

“Okay, folks, we need to talk about this.”

Jerry looked at the other ladies and mouthed “Finally”.

“Mom is being discharged from Columbia at the end of this month,” Norman continued, “We need to figure out what to do. She’s already made the comment that she can’t wait to have her own place again, but the hospital is warning that she’s not really ready to live on her own, not just yet. She’s got to get her strength back up, figure out how to take care of herself again, things like that. Simple chores may exhaust her. So we’ve got to figure something out.”

“I wish we could take her in,” Mary said quietly.

Delmas looked at her and scowled. “There’s no way. We’re barely making it as it is, with a new mouth to feed.”

“I know.” Mary ducked her head. “I was just… I just wish we could.”

Dorothy reached over and put her arm around Mary.

“I don’t think any of us can really take her in for a long period of time,” Norman sighed, looking around the room. “We all have little kids, we’re all struggling to make ends meet. But we have to do something for her.”

“Well, my question is,” Delbert spoke up, “if we find a place that will help her get back on her feet, how are we going to pay for it? I assume it will come down to us since she has no income.”

Everyone looked at each other, but no one spoke.

“You know,” Wanda finally broke the silence, “I could take her to the welfare office and get her signed up for some kind of state…”

“No way!” Norman interrupted, “There’s no way we are going to put our mother on welfare! That’s out of the question!”

“Well now wait a minute, Norman,” Jerry spoke up as she put her hand on his shoulder. “What’s wrong with signing her up for some state aid? She could gain some independence having some of her own money coming in.”

“No! Absolutely not! I’m not going to allow my mother to be

signed up for welfare! We're going to have to come up with something else!"

Neil looked across the table at Delbert. Delbert raised his eyebrows then looked at Ray.

No one said a word.

"Could I say something?" Dorothy raised her hand and waved.

"What's on your mind?" Wanda spoke up before any of the men.

"Putting the money issue aside for a moment, let's get back to possible places where Mom can get some care. My mother knows a lot of businesspeople. Would anyone mind if I ask her if she can come up with anything?"

Ruth Moody, Dorothy's mother, owned an accounting firm in Springfield called "Park Your Problems" and served as contract accountant for several firms in town, in addition to preparing taxes for individuals. Her intimate knowledge of a multitude of businesses made her well connected.

"That's an excellent idea, Dorothy!" Jerry smiled. "Would your mom mind doing that for us?"

"Mom got to know Sarah pretty well in the hospital. I know she'd love to help."

"Thanks, Dorothy," Norman said, calming down. "Now back to this money thing…"

"Norman," Ray interrupted, "How 'bout we just let this money issue wait for a bit. Let's see what Mrs. Moody comes up with, find out how much it costs, then go from there."

Norman looked at Ray, snuffed out the short remains of his cigarette, then looked at Ray again. Jerry squeezed his shoulder.

"Good idea, Ray," Norman sighed, "Everyone in the room okay with that?"

Norman looked at everyone. All the brothers, wide-eyed, looked back and nodded.

"Ladies, you agree?" Norman looked at each woman, Wanda last. Each one nodded.

"Okay then, we'll wait to see what Mrs. Moody finds. Then we will talk about money."

Once Dorothy let her mother know about the situation, Ruth

Moody began to call her business contacts. After several discussions about nursing homes, Ruth talked with a local pharmacist whose mother had stayed with a woman named Gertrude Sullivan after an automobile accident. Gertrude, divorced with grown children, lived in a little two-bedroom bungalow in a quiet neighborhood on North Grant Avenue in Springfield. The pharmacist's mother stayed with Gertrude for several weeks, during which time Mrs. Sullivan boarded one other lady, also recuperating from surgery. Gertrude worked with the boarders, caring for their wounds and helping them to regain their strength so that they could return to living on their own and taking care of themselves.

"How much does Mrs. Sullivan charge for this service?" Ruth asked the pharmacist. "I assume there's room and board, plus medical care."

"She just charges a flat fee," the pharmacist replied. "I believe we paid $50 each month, although I liked giving her an extra $20 from time to time."

"That's not bad. Is she in the phone book?"

"Should be."

"Okay, I'll call her and see if she has an opening. Thanks, Charles."

Only one Gertrude Sullivan appeared in the Springfield phone book, and the address shown was on North Grant, so Ruth dialed the number. Someone answered after five rings.

"Sullivan Residence," an elderly female voice answered.

"Hello, I'm calling for Gertrude Sullivan. Is she available?"

"Yes, just a moment."

After a brief silence, Ruth heard the sound of footsteps, like hard-soled shoes on a wood floor.

"Hello, this is Gertrude."

The soft female voice sounded gentle, kind.

"Hello, Mrs. Sullivan. My name is Ruth Moody. I was referred to you by Charles Wagner. I believe you cared for his mother in the recent past."

"Oh yes, Mrs. Wagner. Delightful lady."

"Yes, ma'am. The reason I am calling, I have a friend, a lady about 61 years old. She was in a fire over a year ago, suffered some pretty awful burns and had to endure skin grafts. She's being released from the hospital at the end of this month, and the doctors say she will need attention after she's out, to get her strength back before she lives on her own. I was told you take in ladies recuperating from things, and I was wondering if you had any space for my friend."

A brief silence.

"Well, Ruth... May I call you Ruth?"

"Yes of course."

"Well, Ruth, I've already got two boarders. I usually don't do three. Tell me again about this lady?"

Ruth repeated her story.

"Hmmm. Well... it sure sounds like this lady needs help. How old did you say she is?"

"She's 61."

"Well... hang on a moment..."

Ruth heard a thump as Gertrude set the phone down. She heard the footsteps walk away from the phone. Then after a few seconds, she heard them coming back.

"Ruth, are you still there?"

"Yes, I'm here."

"Well, I tell you what, if she doesn't mind being in my front parlor rather than a bedroom, I'll take her in. I just don't have a spare bedroom at the moment. I can move some furniture and set up a bed in the parlor."

"I think that would be fine."

"I'll need some time though. When did you say she is being released?"

"She's getting out on May 1."

"That's a Monday. I don't think I can be ready by then. Can she stay with someone till Saturday May 6th? I can take her in on that day."

"Well, she has several sons and daughters. They all work and some have kids, which is why they can't take care of her full time. But I'm sure she can stay with one of them for a few days till you are ready."

"Okay, good. Let's go with that. Now, I need to let you know I charge $50 each month for these ladies. That's room and board, meals, medical, everything. It's due the first of every month."

"That won't be a problem. I'll come by tomorrow and pay for the first two months in advance."

“I appreciate that. I’m always here, so feel free to drop by whenever. I can show you the house, too, show you where she will stay.”

“Okay, thank you, Mrs. Sullivan. This is going to be a big help.”

Upon hearing of the arrangements made by her mother, Dorothy called everyone and told them, including the fact that her mother was paying for the first two months.

“Tell Mrs. Moody we cannot thank her enough,” Norman said, “I’m going to give her a big hug next time I see her.”

31

4:12p.m., April 16
Burge Hospital, Springfield, Missouri

Drenched with sweat, Virginia lay in the recovery room after fifteen hours of hard labor.

The third child I have carried. My second live birth.

A tear ran down her face.

You've got a baby sister, Gary!

With her face away from the door, she didn't see Billy walk into the room until he cleared his throat to get her attention.

"Hey," she said weakly, holding out her hand.

Billy moved close enough to take her hand for a moment then let go, looking around the room, shifting from one foot to the other, then looked back at her.

"I hear it's a girl," he said blandly.

"Yes, she's the most precious thing. Did you see her yet?"

"Any idea what you want to name her?"

"The first thing that popped into my head: Joy," Virginia beamed. "Have you seen her yet?"

Billy snickered.

"Yeah, well," he stammered, "I really wanted a boy. Guess we just have to try again, huh?"

Virginia scowled.

"Billy Joe, are you… are you mad?"

Billy wiped his nose then scratched his head.

"I don't blame you. I just… We'll just have to try again, that's all."

He turned and walked out of the room.

5:28p.m., April 22
Neil and LaVonne Ritter's house

"Oh, Neil, I've been meaning to ask you, what year did you graduate high school? Wasn't it 1959?"

LaVonne's sudden question broke the silence that filled the tiny house as she and Neil enjoyed a dinner of soup and bread. Neil didn't immediately look up.

"Neil?"

Neil set his spoon down, took a sip of tea, and wiped his mouth with his napkin before looking up.

"Well, I guess we never talked about that before."

"No, I guess we haven't, and the question popped into my head earlier today so I wanted to ask you."

Neil picked up his napkin again and cleared his throat.

"Well, I, uh… I was supposed to graduate in '59, yes."

"Supposed to?" LaVonne scowled.

"Well, see, I took art my last semester. And the teacher was a real piece of work. She didn't like me at all, and I didn't like her. So most of the time, I never turned anything in. And I guess because of that she failed me. I flunked art, so I didn't get to graduate."

Neil chuckled, trying to break the tension. LaVonne just stared at him.

"I was so mad, I didn't go back. I left that summer for a while and lived with Norman and Jerry and tried to find a job. Then I went back to Ava, to Mom and Dad's, to help them for a time. That was up till… till the fire…"

Silence.

LaVonne cleared her throat.

"So are you telling me you never got your high school diploma?"

"Right." Neil lowered his head.

LaVonne let out a long sigh.

"I didn't know that. I assume you plan to get your GED?"

"What's a ged?"

"No, it's an abbreviation. G-E-D. It stands for General Educational Development. It's the equivalent of a high school diploma. You take a test and you get your GED."

"Well, I don't care what it stands for, I'm not interested in taking any test. I just… I can't do a bunch of studying with everything else I'm going through."

Neil took another drink of tea, a big gulp.

"Neil Ritter, what are our children going to think about their own education if their father doesn't have his GED? What am I supposed to tell them?"

"I don't believe we have to explain to our children why their father… wait, what did you say?"

"I said what are our children going to think about…"

"Children?" Neil interrupted.

LaVonne looked at him, sighed, then got up from the table and walked over to his chair, stepped behind him and leaned over, wrapping her arms around him.

"Yes, Neil, I said children," she whispered, "I'm pregnant."

May 1, 10:00 a.m.
University Hospital, Columbia, Missouri

Sarah sat in her bed, staring out the window.

"Whatcha thinking, Miss Sarah?" asked Freda, her nurse for the day.

"I'm thinking it's been sixteen months… sixteen long months since the fire. And except for a couple of visits away from here and a few months in the beginning at St. John's, I've spent nearly that entire time here."

"Yes, ma'am."

"And today is my last day…"

Sarah continued to stare out the window. Freda waited.

"No offense, dear, but today feels like I'm getting out of prison." Sarah turned and looked at Freda, grinning. "Mind you, I don't necessarily know what it's like to get out of prison!"

They both shared a chuckle then looked at each other.

"I appreciate everything you've done, Freda. You've been tending to me since I first got here. You put up with my down days, always tried hard to make me smile. Thank you."

"I'll let you in on a little secret, Miss Sarah." Freda winked as she took Sarah's hand. "I always asked to be assigned to your room."

"Oh, honey, that's so sweet." Sarah pulled Freda toward her for a gentle hug.

"Just don't forget about us here. We all love you," Freda whispered, tears running down her cheeks.

"I won't. Thank you so much," Sarah whispered back.

Within a few minutes, Ray and Barbara stepped into the room.

"Hey, y'old bat!" Ray blurted as he walked in, only to get smacked on the arm by Barbara.

Sarah turned and laughed, rising from her bed.

"You ornery thing!" She chuckled as she kissed Ray's cheek and hugged him then turned to Barbara.

"Hey, darlin', you ready to get out of this joint?" Barbara smiled, leaning in to gently hug Sarah.

"You bet! And I'm all packed!" Sarah beamed, pointing to two small bags beside the bed.

"Well, I've already signed the release papers so we are all set!" Ray declared as he leaned over to pick up the bags.

"And your limo is here!" announced an orderly walking in with a wheelchair, "You get one last ride, this time to the car."

Sarah gently sat down in the chair with help from Barbara on one side. Once she was settled in, the orderly spun her around and headed for the door. Freda, still wiping away tears, stood at the door and blew a kiss as Sarah went by.

"We love you, Miss Sarah!"

"Love you, too, dear. Thank you again for everything."

Wheeling into the elevator, Sarah let out a big sigh.

"Doing okay, Mom?" Barbara reached down and grabbed Sarah's hand.

"Oh yes, just happy to be moving on!" Sarah squeezed Barbara's hand.

At the main floor, the door opened and Ray jumped out ahead of everyone else.

"I'll pull the car up to the door, Mom," Ray called back, stepping quickly toward the door.

"Did Ray take today off to come up here? And where are those two precious babies of yours?" Sarah asked as she shifted in her wheelchair.

"Yep, he took today off. Norman couldn't get away today because they are shorthanded at work. Wanda and Dorothy are both near their due dates that they needed to stay close to home. Neil and Delmas couldn't get off work, so here we are! LaVonne and Mary are watching Pam and Steve."

"Well, I really do appreciate you two making such a long trip to come up here and get me."

"We're happy to do it, Mom! And you'll stay with us till Mrs. Sullivan has her room available for you. Just a few days."

"I'm glad. I'll get to see those babies for a bit. I'm really looking forward to meeting Mrs. Sullivan. I hope to see Ruth Moody at some point so that I can thank her personally for all she's done."

"One other person took off work today, too!" a familiar voice spoke up from across the room.

Sarah's eyes lit up as she saw Dr. Charles Lockhart walking toward her, with a big smile on his face and bouquet of flowers in his hand.

"I told you I wanted to be here the day you left this place!"

"Oh, you sweet man!" Sarah leaned up and kissed Lockhart on the cheek.

"These are for you, to celebrate you freedom!" Lockhart smiled as he gave the flowers to Sarah.

"Oh, they are beautiful! Thank you so much, Doctor."

"You're very welcome, Miss Sarah. Norman called me and let me know you were getting out today. I needed a break, so I took the day off and enjoyed getting out to come see you."

"Oh, that ornery son of mine! Thank you so much. It feels good to be taking the next step." Sarah beamed.

Just then, Ray pulled up to the front door and honked the horn.

"I see your ride is here." Lockhart turned toward the door. "Have a safe trip to Springfield, Sarah. Best of luck to you."

"Thank you, Doctor. Thank you for everything you've done.

"It was certainly a pleasure."

The orderly pushed Sarah toward the door as Barbara ran ahead to help Ray get everything situated for the long ride. Moving slowly, Sarah settled into the back seat, and within minutes they were on the highway, heading southwest to Springfield.

32

1:10p.m., May 6
Gertrude Sullivan's House, Springfield, Missouri

Ray drove up Grant Avenue, watching for the Sullivan house.

"There it is!" Barbara declared as Ray slowed. Sarah leaned forward against the window, looking at the pretty little yellow home. All the houses on that block of North Grant had yards with a steep slope up from the sidewalk, little concrete steps with rails, and pretty, manicured lawns. The Sullivan house was a little bungalow nestled amongst several two-story homes. With a pretty covered wooden porch on two sides, it looked welcoming and pleasant.

"There's no place to pull over here, Barbara," Ray said as he checked his rearview mirror to see if anyone was behind him. A brief honk of a horn indicated there was.

"I bet they have an alley around back," Barbara directed. "Turn up here on Nichols Street and see if there's an alley back there."

Ray turned and saw that just past the house on the corner, an alley opened up with access to the back of each house.

"There you go, son! Good thinking, Barbara." Sarah grinned as she reached up and patted Barbara's arm.

"Mom, stay put. I'll get the door," Ray said as he parked the car. "Let's get you in there and then I'll come back out for your stuff."

The back yard was grassy for the first twenty feet from the house, with little wooden flower beds running along the walls. Two old metal lawn chairs sat rusting nearby. A single tall elm tree spread its branches out over most of the yard, hinting at the substantial shade it would provide when the leaves fully bloomed. The rest of the yard, all the way to the alley, was gravel, with a little walkway that led from the parking area to the back door.

"This sure is a cute little place," Sarah said, looking around while Barbara walked slowly with her.

"Sure is. Let's get you inside and out of this wind," Barbara answered.

Just as Ray got to the back door, it was opened by a tall slender gray-haired lady, wearing a long dress, dark stockings and hard-soled shoes.

"Hello, you must be Mr. Ritter. I'm Gertrude Sullivan. Welcome!" Gertrude held out her hand to shake.

"Hello, Mrs. Sullivan," Ray said as he turned, "This is my mother, Sarah Ritter. And my wife Barbara."

"Hello, Sarah, it's so nice to meet you!" Gertrude grasped Sarah's right hand then covered it with her left. "Welcome! I hope you will like it here. We are so pleased to have you staying with us."

"Thank you, I'm so very grateful for you welcoming me like this and offering a place to stay," Sarah said as she looked around.

The back door brought guests into a walled-in porch area which housed the washer and dryer. From there, everyone walked into the spacious kitchen which sported hardwood floors, a large dinner table and cabinetry along two walls.

"Oh my, this is lovely!" Sarah exclaimed, looking around.

"We have all our meals here, and we all eat together. We're like a little family here. I'll introduce you to the other ladies, but first I'd like to show you your room, Sarah."

Together they walked down a short hall toward the front door, and to the left, behind glass doors, was the old parlor.

"This will be your room, Miss Sarah. I hope you like it. Since my other two bedrooms were full, I figured it was time to convert this room into a place to stay."

Sarah's mouth hung open as she walked into the room, with its large, curtained window facing east, pretty floral wallpaper on all the walls, and a bed with headboard and extra pillows.

"I moved this little dresser in for you. I hope it will suffice." Gertrude motioned to the small simple wood dresser against one wall. "And I brought in this wardrobe that belonged to my daughter, for any dresses you might have."

"I do have a couple, thanks to my daughters." Sarah smiled as she continued looking around. "Mrs. Sullivan, this is just lovely. I cannot thank you enough for taking me in."

"Please, you must call me Gertrude. Like I said, we are a little family here, and we're happy to call each other by our first names. We get our groceries delivered from the place down the street. And when you feel up to it, there's a church within walking distance, just up Grant. Other than that, this is all about you getting stronger and healthier and to the point where you can live on your own somewhere."

"Mrs. Sullivan, what about visitors? Is there any requirement on when we can come see her?" Ray asked, looking around the room.

"All I ask is that you phone ahead of time to let us know. I have other ladies living here as well, and we want to know when people are planning to show up so that we can be ready."

"Completely understandable," Barbara agreed. "We will let the rest of the family know."

"I'll get your stuff, Mom," Ray said, turning around to leave the room.

"Sounds like a good time for you to meet the other ladies," Gertrude said as she led Sarah and Barbara out of the room.

6:30p.m.
Norman Ritter's House, Springfield, MO

"You did what?" Norman bellowed as he glared at Wanda.

"I told you," Wanda said calmly, "I went over to Ray's and got Mother and took her over to the welfare office to get her signed up."

"I said before that I do *not* want our mother to be some welfare case!"

"Norman, how else is she going to have any money to live? She's got no income, she's got no belongings. We're having to buy her clothes, toiletries, everything! None of us have the money to support her, and she wouldn't be happy with us paying her way. I know you said you didn't like it, but I went ahead and did it because I think it's the best thing for her."

"I don't like you going around my back to do this, especially when you know I'm against it!"

"Now just cool your jets there, big brother." June stepped forward from her spot against a kitchen cabinet. She and Jim had flown in from Norfolk, Virginia where they were stationed in the Navy. "Norman, if you'll calm down and think about it for a minute, this makes sense. We gotta do something so Mom can have some money of her own, and some insurance. There's nothing wrong with her being signed up to receive government money. If you think about it, Jim and I live on government money, being in the military. And you even received government money when you were in the army."

Norman ducked his head.

"Now, you need to get off Wanda's back and accept the fact that this is right for Mom."

Silence.

"Norman?" June stepped closer to Norman and put her hands on her hips.

Norman's face softened as he looked up.

"You always were a tough little shit," he winked. "Alright. I still don't care much for it. But you're right, we can't support her, and she needs some independence. Wanda, sorry I got so mad."

"That's alright, Norman. But I knew it was going to be the right thing to do, no matter how mad you were at me."

"Alright. Let's eat," Norman said as he lit another cigarette.

6:30p.m.
Billy and Virginia McCormack's house, Ozark, Missouri

"Virginia! Get in here!"

Virginia, busily washing dishes in the kitchen, dropped her dishcloth and ran into the bedroom, fearing Billy was hurt. Instead, he was standing by her dresser, hands on his hips, scowling at her.

"What the hell is this?" he yelled, pointing at her antique vanity.

"What is what, Billy?"

"You know damn well what I'm talking about! What are these pictures doing here?"

Down in the bottom right corner of the mirror on her vanity she had taped small photos of Dewey and Gary. Normally hidden by a vase with artificial red and white carnations, the two photos were discovered after the vase shifted some time earlier, no doubt while Virginia put on her makeup that morning.

Virginia's heart began to pound.

"Those have always been there, Billy."

"I've never seen them! What have you been doing, hiding them from me?"

"Well no, I… I…"

"You're still in love with him, aren't you! You still love that damn hillbilly!"

"But… but he died! Don't you understand, he and Gary were taken from me!"

"You are married to *me*! They are *dead*! Can't you get that through that thick skull of yours?"

Terrified, Virginia couldn't come up with a word to say.

"I'm going out! If those pictures are still there when I get back, I'm getting rid of them myself. It's been over a year, you need to get over it and move on!"

Billy stomped out of the room. Virginia sat down on the bed, cradling her abdomen. The front door slammed.

Dear God, I hope this gets better. Maybe if I put the pictures away he'll be nicer.

She got up from the bed and carefully pulled the pictures off the mirror. Looking around, she opened the right drawer of her vanity, and stuck the pictures to the side of the drawer, way back out of sight.

I'll never part with my pictures. Never.

33

August 25 – 8:00 a.m.
Gertrude Sullivan's house, Springfield, Missouri

Sarah walked into the dining room and noticed Gertrude sitting at the kitchen table with her back to her.

"Good morning, Miss Gertrude." Sarah tried to keep from startling her.

Gertrude jumped then turned around in her chair.

"Oh, Miss Sarah! I wasn't expecting you to be up and about just yet!"

She looked Sarah over.

"You're fully dressed! Lookin' like someone who's planning to go somewhere! You got something in mind?"

Sarah looked down at her dress and shoes then looked back up at Gertrude with a smile.

"I was just wondering if you needed anything from the store. Thought I'd like to walk down to the market this morning. You know, before it gets too hot."

Gertrude smiled.

"I think that would be a fine idea, Sarah. A walk like that would be good for you. Are you sure you feel up to it?"

"You bet," Sarah beamed with a slight chuckle. "I'd really like to give it a try. If it gets to be too much, I'll come back. But I'd sure like to try."

"I kinda thought you might be ready for something like that. Hang on, let me make a list."

Gertrude made a small list of light items and gave it to Sarah.

"Just tell them to put it on my bill." Gertrude smiled.

"Okay. I'm off!" Sarah declared as she stepped out the door.

Thornbury's Solo Market, located just a little over two blocks from the Sullivan house, had been a neighborhood grocery store for nearly a decade. Gertrude usually took advantage of their delivery service for neighbors in the immediate area and stocked up on all necessities. But with Sarah wanting to venture out on her own, she came up with a simple list of items that would be light to carry, including eggs, bread, butter, and licorice as a treat.

In the front yard, Sarah held the iron pipe handrails as she slowly made her way down the three steps to the sidewalk, then stopped and looked around. Several children were playing in a yard across the street, and a neighbor to the south was busy mowing. Sarah closed her eyes and breathed in, her nostrils filled with the smell of freshly cut grass. The hot, humid days of August brought on the feeling of rising humidity early in the day, and Sarah breathed out as the heat from the sidewalk and street in front of her warned that she should be on her way so that she could return to the house before the temperatures rose much more.

Turning to her left, she walked north past the Jenkins and Halloway homes to the corner of Grant and Nichols. Traffic was minimal, with no one on Nichols at the stop sign, so she shuffled across the intersection and continued up Grant Street. After less than a block, she came to Grant Avenue Baptist Church and stopped in front of their steps and dug out a hanky from her pocket, wiping perspiration from her neck.

"Sarah Elizabeth, gonna be a warm one," she said quietly to herself, smiling. "Yes, my dear Orville, it sure is."

With still a block to go, Sarah crossed at State Street to the other side of Grant and continued north to the store. She noticed the parking lot was nearly empty as she approached the door and, upon opening, was happy to discover a pleasant rush of cool air from the air conditioning within. Since it was her first trip to the store, she took her time walking every aisle. At the produce section, she marveled at the large navel oranges on display and decided to vary from the list and grabbed four for Gertrude, the other two ladies in the house and herself.

Stopping at the meat counter, she ran her hands along the cool glass as she looked at the trays of steaks, pork, chicken, and ground beef.

"May I help you, ma'am?" a friendly voice bellowed from behind the counter.

Sarah looked up to see a tall young man leaning over, smiling at her.

"Oh, no thank you, son," Sarah smiled. "I'm new to this store and was enjoying looking at everything you have."

"Well, let me know if you need anything."

Sarah continued around the rest of the store, collecting up the items on her list. When she got to the eggs, she opened up the top package and looked in, shaking her head.

"All white. Not a brown one in the bunch," she muttered to herself. "Back on the farm we always saw brown and never a white one!"

She put the package in her cart and continued shopping.

After making her way up and down every aisle, she approached the counter to check out and set all of her items out. A young clerk looked up at her as she put the last of her plunder on the counter.

"Good morning, ma'am!" The young girl flashed a bright smile.

"Good morning, dear!" Sarah smiled back. "I don't know if you need to know it now or after you've rung all this up, but this is to be a charge on Mrs. Sullivan's account."

"That's fine! I'm happy to handle that now."

The store manager, standing nearby, walked over to the counter.

"Ma'am, did I hear you say that this is a charge for Mrs. Sullivan?"

"Yes, is that okay?" Sarah frowned, afraid that there might be an issue with the account.

"Of course, ma'am." He smiled, sticking out his hand to shake Sarah's. "I'm Fred Aimsly, the store manager."

"It's a pleasure to know you, Mr. Aimsly. I'm Sarah Ritter, and I'm staying at Mrs. Sullivan's house. She's taking care of me after… well…" Sarah looked down, stumbling with her words. "She's taking very good care of me."

"Well, Mrs. Ritter, I'm glad to know you are staying with her.

Did you walk here today?"

"Yes sir, I decided I wanted to get out and walk a bit. I've never been to your store before, and I thought today would be a good day for it. I'm getting stronger and healing very nicely, and I hope to be living on my own very soon. Gotta get out and walk if I'm going to live on my own. I don't intend to just sit around all the time, Mr. Aimsly."

"I understand." Fred smiled. "Mrs. Ritter, would you like for one of my boys to carry these for you? It's heating up out there and you've got a couple of blocks to walk."

"No, sir. This is a pretty light load and I'm happy to carry it back. But thank you so much for the offer. I'll look forward to returning to this store again in the near future, and perhaps then when I have more to carry, I will take you up on your kind offer.

"Very well, Mrs. Ritter." Fred patted her hand then let go. "I'll look forward to seeing you again. Please be careful on your way back."

"Thank you, dear!"

As the manager walked away, Sarah turned to the clerk, who had already rung everything up and had it waiting in a paper bag.

"You sure you got that okay?" the clerk asked as Sarah picked up the bag and adjusted it in her arms.

"Yes, thank you!" Sarah smiled, proud of her accomplishment, and stepped out into the hot August morning.

"Whew! I swear it's ten degrees hotter now than it was when I walked in there!" Sarah declared to herself as she began her walk back to the house. She began to tire crossing Nichols Street, and was glad that home was just three houses away.

Sarah's health and strength continued to improve. When it became clear that she was nearly ready to live on her own, Ruth Moody, once again called into action to help with her many contacts, located a small efficiency apartment for rent, located behind a large old house on South Street near downtown Springfield. The owner, Mrs. Geneva Bussard who lived in the main house, advertised often for tenants in the local newspaper. After touring the little apartment, Ruth felt it would suit Sarah's needs well and be close enough to others that she could get help if needed. She could even have her own telephone, connected by party line to the main house.

By March 1, 1962, Sarah was settled into her apartment.

April 6, 6:25 p.m.
Bussard House/Sarah's Apartment

The phone rang four times before being answered.

"Hello?"

"Hello, you old bat!" Delmas hollered from the other end.

"I beg your pardon!" Mrs. Bussard, who picked up the phone before Sarah, was a bit indignant over the greeting.

"Oh my, I'm so sorry, Mrs. Bussard. I thought you were my mother. This is Delmas, one of Mrs. Ritter's younger sons. I apologize for calling you that. I was wondering if I could talk to my mother."

"Well… I will go out and get Mrs. Ritter for you, young man."

"Thank you, Mrs. Bussard." Delmas turned several shades of red while Mary stood behind him, suppressing a laugh.

After a few moments, the line clicked and Delmas heard Sarah's voice.

"Hello, son!" Sarah sounded jovial.

"Hi, Mom, just wanted to check on you," Delmas said. They both heard the line click again as Mrs. Bussard hung up.

"Son, what in the world did you say? Mrs. Bussard was madder than an old wet hen!" Sarah chuckled.

"Oh, man, I thought I'd be funny and yelled 'hello, you old bat!'"

"Oh, good lord! Sounds like you'd better check to make sure it's me next time! She left here in a huff. I'm thinking she will have more to say on the subject later," Sarah laughed.

"Yeah," Delmas chuckled, "Hey I was thinking about packing up Mary and Debbie and this new little fella of ours and coming over to see you!"

"Oh my, yes, I want to see that new boy of yours! Bring Granny her babies!" Sarah said, practically squealing.

Sarah had five grandkids before The Fire, courtesy of Norman, Ray, Dewey, and Elda June. After The Fire and up to the time of her moving into the apartment, five more entered the world, the newest being Doug, son of Delmas and Mary, who was born in mid-March.

Within an hour, Sarah sat happily on the couch across from Delmas and Mary, with her newest grandson in her arms, and a granddaughter snuggled up against her side.

"How does it feel to finally have your own place, Mom?" Mary asked, smiling as she watched Sarah holding the baby.

"It feels good, Mary. It feels really good. I'm still getting used to it a bit, and I'm finding I can't cook worth a hoot on a gas stove," Sarah laughed, "But it feels really good."

34

June 3, 2:32 a.m.
St. John's Hospital Emergency Room

LaVonne ran from her car into the emergency room entrance, stopping at the desk.

"I'm here to see Neil Ritter," she gasped, out of breath from her run and the panic from being awakened in the middle of the night to hear that Neil collapsed at work.

"Hold on just a moment, ma'am. Are you his wife?"

"Yes." LaVonne tried to calm down as the nurse looked through her paperwork.

"He's in Room 6. You can see him."

"Thank you."

LaVonne walked quickly down the cold corridor, past the little exam areas, starkly lit by bright overhead lights, to Room 6. There, lying on the bed with his eyes closed, an IV in his arm and an oxygen mask over his nose and mouth, was Neil. Looking him over, she reached out and gently grasped his hand, which was resting on his abdomen.

My God, is he even alive?

"Neil?" she whispered.

Neil's eyes fluttered but didn't open.

"Hello, my sweet…" he said weakly.

4:15 a.m.

Neil, awake and sitting up in bed, held LaVonne's hand.

"Mr. Ritter, from what I understand, you've been dealing with recurring nightmares and other stresses related to a fire that happened a couple of years ago," the doctor said, looking at his notes.

"Yes, sir. The Fire was in October of 1959. I lost three family members, two that night, and my father a couple of days later," Neil answered.

"I'm very sorry." The doctor finally looked up from his notes. "You know, normally when we experience trauma, we go into something called shock. That usually erases some of the worst parts of the experience from our memory, helping our brain to cope with the trauma. Since you seem to recall everything from that night and continue to have vivid nightmares, you obviously didn't go into shock at any time since the event."

"That's our understanding of it, Doctor," LaVonne chimed in.

"Well, it appears your collapse this morning at work is in direct correlation to all those memories and trauma swirling around in your head, Mr. Ritter. The mind is an amazing thing, but if it harbors memories too horrifying to bear, it can harm you. To put it all in layman's terms, your mind is hurting, and now it's starting to take it out on your body. If something doesn't happen soon to remedy that, all this stress and trauma, quite frankly, will kill you."

Neil and LaVonne looked at each other, then back to the doctor.

"Mr. Ritter, have you ever considered talking with someone?"

"What do you mean, Doctor? Like a shrink?"

The doctor chuckled for a moment.

"Well, I don't think they particularly care for the term 'shrink' but yes, a professional in the field, a psychiatrist, would most likely be able to help you with the memories of your trauma. They are making great strides these days in the field of mental health. And, Mr. Ritter, it is my professional assessment as a doctor that you need to get some help to relieve you of these traumatic memories."

"Can you recommend anyone, Doctor?"

"Yes I can. A colleague of mine, Dr. Hans Hulston, specializes in trauma patients. I can contact him and see if he has an opening for you."

"That would be great," Neil said, trying to smile. "I appreciate the help. If he can relieve me of all of this stuff in my head, I'd be grateful."

"Okay, I'll call him."

June 20, 2:10 p.m.
Hulston Clinic, Springfield, Missouri

Neil sat straight, hands on his knees in Dr. Hulston's office, looking around the room. A massive antique oak desk and long brown leather couch dominated the room. Bookcases stood on either side of the desk, with a large window between them, the thick curtains drawn so that the only light in the room was from two lamps that sat on end tables between the couch and chairs on either end. Paintings of mountains and other landscapes dotted the walls.

Suddenly the door opened and Dr. Hulston entered the room. Neil stood up to shake hands as the doctor's six-foot-five-inch frame towered over him.

"Ah, Mr. Ritter, I am so pleased to meet you!" Hulston exclaimed.

"Pleasure to meet you, too, sir." Neil smiled as he settled back down into his seat.

"Mr. Ritter…"

"Neil, please."

Hulston smiled.

"Neil, before we begin our visit, would you be more comfortable lying down on the couch, or you are welcome to sit in one of these more comfortable chairs." Hulston waved toward the couch area.

"A chair would be fine. I'm afraid that couch would lull me to sleep, Doc," Neil joked, trying to get past his nervousness.

"Fine, fine, go ahead and take a seat then. And I must ask you a very serious question. Neil, do you want anything we discuss here shared with your wife or whatever next-of-kin you prefer?"

"No. Never."

June 27, 5:22 p.m.
Neil and LaVonne Ritter's house

"How did your appointment with Dr. Hulston go today?" LaVonne asked as she set a glass of tea on the table by Neil's plate.

"Okay, I guess. He wants to try something," Neil said between bites.

LaVonne waited for Neil to voluntarily continue talking, but after taking a few more bites, it was obvious that he needed a little prodding.

"Neil, honey, what exactly does he want to try?"

"Well…" Neil took a long drink of tea then let out a deep sigh. "He wants to try shock therapy."

"Shock therapy!" LaVonne's eyes grew big. "Seriously?"

"Yeah. He says it's worked well to help with short-term memory of recent events. He thinks with several treatments, it should help with memories from The Fire."

"Did he say anything about side effects from the treatments?"

"He said I may be a bit confused after I awaken. But that should pass within minutes."

"So what did you tell him?"

"I said let's try it. If it will help me get past all this, get me to where I can finally cope, I'm all for it. I gotta admit, it's a little scary, but I'm willing to try. I gotta try something, love. We can't keep living like this."

"Okay, Neil. I'm with you all the way, love. When does he want to do this?"

"He wants to start Monday. Three times a week for six weeks."

"Jesus, honey. That's a lot!"

"Yeah. It is."

July 2, 3:00 p.m.
Hulston Clinic

"Just try to breathe easy, Mr. Ritter," the nurse said, strapping down his arms and legs. "We have to secure you to the bed, just in case your motor reflexes react to the treatment. You might take a swing at us."

"Okay," Neil said, struggling to remain calm, choosing to stare into the light directly above him. He wiggled his toes and moved his fingers as he felt the straps tighten, restricting his movement.

This is like one of those scary movies...

Dr. Hulston walked into the room as the nurse ran a strap across Neil's forehead and began to tighten it down.

"Ah, Mr. Ritter! Today we begin! We want to make you as comfortable as possible. Try not to be nervous."

"Yeah, that's the tough part," Neil joked, his voice cracking. "Doc, are you going to give me any kind of sedative? You know, something calming?"

Hulston shook his head.

"I'm afraid not. You see, Neil, any sedative might inhibit or block brain activity that we are trying to reach. Do not worry, it only lasts a couple of minutes and you'll be fine. We will do eighteen of these treatments over the next six weeks and have you feeling better."

Neil's pulse quickened.

My God, no sedative!

"Open wide for me, Mr. Ritter," the nurse said quietly. Neil opened his mouth as a long leather strap was brought across his mouth and secured on both sides of the bed.

"This will keep you from biting your tongue or cracking a tooth."

Oh my God, I'm... I'm... This is awful. I can't move at all.

"Okay, Neil, we are going to place two electrodes on either side of your temple, and will begin the procedure. You're going to be just fine."

Neil, wide-eyed and breathing hard, continued to stare at the light as he felt two soft pads on his temples.

No! No! No! This is not...

"Ok, Nurse. Begin."

3:10 p.m.

Hmmft. Muh. Muh Hmmft Puh... L... La... Light... B... Br... Bri... Bright...

"Mr. Ritter? Mr. Ritter? We are all through, Mr. Ritter!"

Sss... Sssss... Si... Six... Six m... Six more... Six more w... Six more weeks...

September 29, 8:12 a.m.
Neil and LaVonne Ritter's house

Neil and LaVonne sat across from each other at the little table in the kitchen. He stared at the toast on his plate. LaVonne watched him quietly.

"Neil… Neil…"

He finally looked up, a hint of a tear in his eye.

"Neil, honey, do you feel like the treatments helped at all? Have they erased some of the memories?"

He stared at her for a moment.

"No… Not one bit."

35

March 18, 1964 – 6:40 a.m.
Garland and Lula Dye's house, Ozark, Missouri

Lula's brow furrowed as Virginia eased herself onto the chair at the breakfast table.

"Honey, that's the third time you've thrown up since you got here… thirty minutes ago."

"Yeah," Virginia whispered, then took a sip of water, "Plus twice earlier this morning."

Lula sat back in her chair, crossed her arms, and grinned.

"You're pregnant again."

"Yeah… I think so…"

7:00 a.m.
Neil and LaVonne Ritter's house, Springfield, Missouri

LaVonne watched Neil trying to get through his breakfast.

"Big day today, Neil! How do you feel?"

"Pretty good. Nervous."

"Don't worry about it. You'll do great. I'm proud of you for finally doing this. I know you're nervous now, but in the long run you'll be glad you got your GED. It's important."

"Yeah. I just hope there isn't anything weird on there. I've studied as much as I know to do…"

He looked out the window for a moment.

"What if they throw something at me, something I haven't studied for?"

"It's an all-day test, right?"

"Right."

"And you get to come home for lunch, right?"

"Right."

"Well then if anything trips you up, we can talk about it over lunch, then you can go back and take care of it!"

Neil turned and looked back at LaVonne.

"You sure?"

"Of course I'm sure, Neil. You're going to be fine. Now relax and eat, you need some food in your belly to be able to think."

11:47 a.m.

LaVonne ran to the door when she heard Neil pull into the driveway.

"Well, how did it go so far?"

Neil's eyes were wide and he looked pale.

"There's fractions on the test. How the hell do you do fractions?"

"Sit down and eat. I'll teach you fractions. Don't sweat it, Neil."

4:10 p.m.

Neil tried his best to suppress a grin as he walked into the house. LaVonne had just settled Patricia in her chair and gave her some cereal when she turned to kiss Neil.

"Well, how did it go? Don't keep us in suspense here!"

Unable to hold it in anymore, Neil cracked a big smile.

"87. I got an 87 on the test. I passed! I got my GED!"

36

January 19, 1965, 10:05a.m.
Ozark, Missouri

Virginia pulled her scarf closer to her face as she braced herself against the cold northerly wind. The walk to the Christian County Courthouse, only three blocks from her little house, felt like miles that morning. The temperature outside struggled to reach freezing. The clouds, gray, heavy and overcast, mirrored the dark, downtrodden feeling in her heart as she pushed against the wind, determined to reach the looming structure coming into view.

"Dear God, I hope he's there," she whispered to herself as she reached the door to the courthouse.

Virginia had tolerated all she could. Now she felt that not only was she in danger, but her two young children were also at risk. It had to end. She knew her first stop had to be at the office of the one man she knew would stop at nothing to protect her and her children: Sheriff L.E. "Buff" Lamb.

Lamb, an Ozark citizen since 1945, became the town's first marshal and helped develop the Ozark Police Department, which he served for nearly 20 years. Recently elected as county sheriff, Lamb now had responsibility to maintain law and order in all of Christian County. He was already notorious. Before getting into law enforcement, his hobbies included bull riding, bronco busting, and jumping his motorcycle over burning buildings and rows of cars. Lamb was fearless, and by 1965 everyone in Christian County knew they didn't want to get on his bad side. Always armed with two revolvers and a long metal flashlight, Lamb thought nothing of popping a teenage boy on the head if he thought the boy had circled the square one time too many on a Friday night.

Virginia walked into the sheriff's office, still shaking off the cold from her walk. Fumbling with her coat, she got tangled with the sash and accidently pushed the door harder than she intended. It closed with a bang, which got the attention of everyone in the office.

"Sorry, folks," Virginia smiled meekly as an imposing figure approached her from the right.

"May I help you ma'am?"

Virginia turned and found Sheriff Lamb standing in front of her with his hand out. Tall in his cowboy boots and hat, with a toothpick rolling around the side of his mouth, a slight smile crept across his face.

He seems nice.

"Sheriff Lamb, I'm sorry to bother you, but I was wondering if you might have a moment? I think I need your help."

"Please, step into my office." Lamb stepped aside and motioned toward the old wooden door. Once inside, he closed the door as Virginia settled into the chair across the desk from his.

"I'm sorry, ma'am, but I did not catch your name."

"My name is Virginia McCormack. I live just a couple of blocks away, on Oak Street."

"What can I do for you, Mrs. McCormack?"

"Well, Sheriff, I… well…" Virginia lowered her head as she fought back tears. "Sheriff… I'm going to have to… to divorce my husband. And… And I'm a bit scared."

Lamb scowled as he leaned forward.

"Mrs. McCormack, what's going on at your house?"

Tearfully, Virginia told him the entire story. She shared how she lost Dewey and Gary, plus the baby she had been carrying that night back in 1959. She told him how she moved west to try to rebuild her life, and how she met Billy. Then she told him how they had come back to Ozark to be near her parents, gave birth to Joy, then how things began to unravel. She told about Billy's jealousy of her memories of Dewey and Gary. She explained everything, about getting pregnant again, how she hoped another baby might settle him down, and how nothing had changed since little Timmy was born.

"At this point, Sheriff, I know that I've got to end this. I don't want to, but I can't keep living like this. I've got to end it." Virginia wiped her eyes with her hanky again.

"Mrs. McCormack, have you filed for divorce yet?" Sheriff Lamb was still leaning toward her, arms on his desk.

"No, sir. That's my next stop. I thought perhaps Mr. Roller might be able to help me."

"I've known Arnie Roller for years." Lamb cracked a brief smile. "You tell him you've been to see me, and he will take good care of you."

"Thank you, Sheriff."

Lamb sighed.

"Mrs. McCormack, if you feel like you're in danger, I can't let you go back to your house without doing something about it. I'm obligated by law to take action. Do you understand that?"

"Yes, sir. I don't think that's necessary yet. I think if I divorce him, it'll be okay."

"Are you sure, Mrs. McCormack? I want you to be sure. Because I'm serious, I can't let you go back home if you think you are in danger."

"I'm sure, Sheriff." Virginia nodded. "As a matter of fact, I'd like to ask you to please call me Virginia from now on rather than Mrs. McCormack. I'm not going to be Mrs. McCormack for much longer."

"That's good," Lamb smiled and nodded. "Virginia, you're on my radar. If he gives you one moment of trouble, one moment of feeling like you or your children are in danger, all you need to do is call me."

"Thank you, Sheriff. I appreciate that."

"Okay." Lamb got up from his desk and turned to grab his coat. Virginia stood up as well and they walked to the office door.

"Miss Virginia, you head on over to Roller's office. Your discussion with him will take a while. You keep me posted on how things are going, and if you need me to handle McCormack, I'm just a phone call away."

"Thank you so much, Sheriff. I knew you could help me."

Lamb gently took her hand.

"Miss Virginia, I'm known around these parts as one mean son of a bitch. But, ma'am, I am here to protect you and your children. And if I have to be a mean son of a bitch to do it, then that's my lot in life. My door is always open to you and your children. If you need anything, or if he gives you any more trouble, I'm right here."

"Thank you so much, Sheriff. You know, I've felt helpless since all this took a turn for the worse. I feel stronger now. I know it's all going to be okay."

"Miss Virginia, after all you've been through, I can testify that you are indeed a strong woman." Lamb tipped his hat.

11:00a.m.
Arnie Roller's office

At Arnie Roller's law office, located on the west side of the square just a short walk from the courthouse, Virginia signed a petition for divorce.

"Miss Virginia, you said your husband is out of work," Roller said after she completed signing the papers. "If I may ask, how are you set to support yourself and your children?"

"Well, Mr. Roller, I've been working as a waitress at the café in Crank's in Springfield. We rent that house that we've been in, and my parents are very helpful."

"Okay, that's good. You've got a plan. Let me know if you need anything. I'm going to draw up the paperwork this afternoon. You come back tomorrow and sign everything, and I'll push this through. And in the future if you put in an application anywhere, you are more than welcome to put myself and Sheriff Lamb down for personal references."

"Really? Oh, thank you so much, Mr. Roller." Virginia sat back in her chair and let out a big sigh. "You know, I felt like the weight of the world was on my shoulders this morning, Mr. Roller."

"Call me Arnie," He grinned.

"Okay, Arnie… but now, after talking with you and Sheriff Lamb, I feel better. I feel strong again. I feel like I can do this, and that things are going to be alright."

"You are most certainly correct, Virginia." Roller got up to walk her out of his office, "Things are going to be just fine. And if you need anything else, please don't hesitate to let me know."

January 25, 1965, 1:10p.m.
Virginia's house, Ozark, Missouri

Wonder if that bitch had the locks changed yet.

Billy looked over his shoulder around the neighborhood as he put his key in the lock of the house that he previously shared with Virginia. The divorce had been final for a few days. When she handed him the papers, he angrily gathered up his things and left. But today, he was back for revenge.

Happy to see his key still worked, he threw the door open and walked in. He stepped on several of the children's toys that were scattered about, breaking them as he stomped around the place. He walked into the bedroom he had shared with Virginia, looking for something to destroy. He stopped when he looked at her dresser. There, leaning against the mirror, were two photographs of Dewey and Gary.

"Well, lookee here," Billy sneered, grabbing the photos. "I've had about enough of you two."

He grabbed the two pictures, folded them in his fist, and stomped out the front door and jumped in his car.

Driving to the Ozark City Park along the Finley River, Billy looked down at the now-crinkled photos lying in the seat next to him.

"I should have done this a long time ago."

Pulling into the park, Billy drove to an area close to the river with easy access to the bank. The Finley flowed near flooding condition, due to recent rains. It ran fast and noisy as Billy stomped over the riverbank, clutching the photos in his fist. Stopping a few inches from the rushing water, he held up the ruined images.

"I hope you two know how to swim. Good riddance."

With a laugh, he threw the crumpled photos into the river, watching them roll around in the churning water until they disappeared. With a quick nod, he turned, got back in his car, and drove to Virginia's house and waited for her to return after work. Settling in on the couch in the living room, he cracked open a beer he had left behind when he moved out.

4:45p.m.

Virginia pulled up in front of her house, horrified to see Billy's car in the driveway. She took a deep breath, got out of her car, and walked in. There sat Billy, on the couch, with the children's toys he had stepped on, strewn about.

"Nice car, baby. Is it new?" he sneered.

"It's used." She glared as she removed her scarf. "Daddy cosigned with me for it."

"Well, how about that. Daddy to the rescue."

"Why are you here?"

"Oh, I just came to get a few things," Billy mocked as he looked around, "Take care of a little unfinished business."

"You don't have any unfinished business here, Billy."

"I don't anymore."

She stared at him for a moment. Then it dawned on her.

Oh dear God. He's always been jealous of Dewey. My pictures!

She ran into her bedroom as Billy laughed. She screamed when she saw that the pictures were gone.

"You heartless bastard!" she yelled, running back into the living room. "What did you do with my pictures?"

"Oh, you know, I just took them for a drive… They decided they wanted to take a swim…"

"What? You did what?"

"That's right, little lady!" Billy jumped up from the couch. "I sent your precious Dewey and Gary for a swim! I'm tired of living under the shadow of their ghosts! So I took them down to the park and threw them in the river! Where they belong! Quit spending your life thinking about dead people! You shoulda been thinking about me!"

"You heartless animal!" Virginia cried as she stormed out the door.

"Where you gonna run now, baby? Who's gonna help you? You can't bring 'em back, you know! Good luck! I'll be here when decide you to come back! I'm not going anywhere!"

Tears running down her face, Virginia jumped in her car and sped off to find the one person she knew she needed at this moment: Sheriff Lamb.

Pulling into the lot for the courthouse, she ran in to find the sheriff.

If he's not here, I'm going to drive till I find him.

Running into the office, she surprised everyone as she stood there, panting and crying. The lady at the desk picked up the phone immediately.

"Sheriff, we need you out here fast."

Within seconds, Lamb came charging out of his office.

"Miss Virginia, what is it?"

Virginia fell into his arms.

"Oh, Sheriff! He came back! Billy came back! The… the locks hadn't been changed yet… on the house! He… he got in! He… he took my pictures… the pictures of my husband and little boy who died in the fire that I told you about!"

She began to calm down a bit to talk.

"The pictures are gone. He said he took them and threw them in the Finley. What kind of man does something like that?"

Sheriff Lamb grabbed her by the shoulders.

"Virginia, where are your children?"

"They are still over at my parents' place. I hadn't picked them up yet. I just got off work and wanted to spend a few moments at the house before I went to get them. He was there. The kids are fine for the moment at my parents' house."

"Miss Virginia, I assume you want me to get him out of your house?"

"Yes, please. Sheriff I hate to ask you to do that. He's a monster. He's nearly seven feet tall, 350 pounds. He's a gorilla. And he's got a pistol. He always carries a pistol."

"I've handled worse, Miss Virginia, believe me. This ole country boy ain't scared of nobody. Now here's what I want you to do. You go over to your parents' place and take care of your little ones. Stay there till I call. Leave us their phone number. I'm going over to that house and I'm going to get him out of there. And I'll make certain he knows he is never to come back here. Okay?"

"Okay, Sheriff. Thank you. I'm sorry to cause so much trouble, I…"

"Shhh, now don't talk like that," Sheriff Lamb interrupted. "Like I told you before, my job is to protect citizens like you. You haven't caused any trouble."

Virginia ducked her head and left without another word. Drying her tears as she drove to Garland and Lula's house a few blocks away, she worried about Sheriff Lamb.

6:32p.m.
Garland and Lula Dye's house, Ozark, Missouri

After hugging her kids, she told her parents about the unexpected encounter with Bill and about Sheriff Lamb's promise to take care of things. Garland and Lula were speechless, and everyone waited for the phone to ring with news.

After nearly an hour, the call came. Garland answered the phone.

"Mr. Dye?"

"Yes."

"This is Sheriff Lamb. Is Miss Virginia still at your house with her children?"

"Yes, sir."

"May I come over and visit with all of you, to let you know what has happened?"

"Yes, sir. Come on over."

Garland hung up the phone and turned to his anxious wife and daughter.

"The sheriff is coming over to tell us what happened."

Less than a minute later, Lamb's car pulled up in front of the house.

Virginia answered the door and let him in then introduced him to her parents. Lula invited the sheriff to sit down. He removed his cowboy hat as he settled in on the couch while the rest of them quickly found chairs.

"Well, folks, I wanted to let all of you know how this went down." He turned to Virginia. "You were right, he's a big ole boy."

Virginia grimaced.

"I decided not to take any chances and entered the home with my pistol drawn. I found Mr. McCormack sitting on the couch. He flinched a little when he saw me come in but didn't go for his pistol. I had him remove it, and it is now in my possession. Then we had us a nice little chat."

"A nice little chat," Garland echoed.

"Yes, sir." Lamb turned to look at Garland. "We talked about the fact that the house was no longer his, and that he was trespassing.

We also talked about how mean it was to step on the kids' toys and to destroy those photos you had."

Lamb turned back to look at Virginia, next to him on the couch.

"Miss Virginia, he showed no remorse for destroying those pictures."

"I'm not surprised." Virginia shook her head.

"No, ma'am," Lamb continued, "I charged Mr. McCormack with trespassing, arrested him, and took him to jail."

Everyone's eyes widened.

"He paid $50 bail then we went back to your house. I required him to give me his key to your place, he got in his car, and I followed him to the county line. He's now gone."

Sighing, Virginia lowered her head.

"When I got back to my office, before I called you to come over here, I called your landlord, Mr. Morgan."

Startled, Virginia looked back up at the sheriff.

"You know Mr. Morgan?"

"Yes, ma'am, I sure do. I told Eldon about what happened, and I told him to change the locks for you immediately. He said he'd pick some up and put them on this evening. He thinks very highly of you and wants to do everything he can to keep you safe."

"Oh, Sheriff, you don't know how much all this means to me. To us," Virginia reached over and grasped Lamb's hand.

"It's my pleasure to help," Lamb said, patting her hand on top of his. "Now where are those two young'uns of yours? I'd like to see them!"

Lula perked up.

"They are in the other room. I heard them waking up from their nap a moment ago. I'll go get them."

"Can I get you something to drink, Sheriff? A glass of water or tea?" Garland offered.

"No thank you, Mr. Dye. I'll need to get going but I wanted to see these little kids first."

Lula emerged from the back bedroom carrying Timmy in her arms while leading little Joy, who was rubbing her eyes.

"Joy, can you say hi to Mr. Lamb?" Virginia leaned in to her daughter.

Joy gave a quiet "hi" and a quick wave as the sheriff grinned and said hello.

"And this is little Timmy," Virginia said, taking Tim from her mom's arms and bringing him over to show Sheriff Lamb.

"Oh, he's a fine lookin' boy, Miss Virginia. And Miss Joy is just as pretty as she can be," Lamb said, rising from the couch, "Y'all let me know if there is anything else I can do. But I think your troubles with Mr. McCormack are pretty much over."

"Thank you so much, Sheriff," Garland said as he shook hands and showed Lamb out.

37

March 5, 8:30am
Neil and LaVonne Ritter's house

"Did you have any specific plans today, Neil?" LaVonne asked then blew across her coffee to take a sip.

"Not really. Just kinda thought we would enjoy this nice day together. Why?"

"I talked with Jerry yesterday, and she said that she and Norman ran into Virginia the other day. Apparently she's working at Crank's Drug Store in the Glen Isle Center as a waitress in their cafe. I thought maybe you and I could go have lunch there and hopefully visit with her."

Neil drew in a deep breath, sat down his coffee cup, and leaned back in his chair, turning to gaze out the window.

"You know, I haven't seen her since I got out of the hospital back in November of '59." he sighed. "It would sure be nice to see her. But it brings back a lot of memories, too."

LaVonne didn't say anything. She just watched as Neil continued to stare out the window.

He's somewhere far away... remembering that night.

After several seconds, he turned back to look at her.

"Let's do it. I think I'd like to see her." Neil smiled slightly then leaned forward to take another sip of coffee. "Yeah, I'd like to see her."

12:40 p.m.
Crank's Drug Store, Springfield, MO

The after-church lunch crowd filled nearly every table available in the simple little café inside Crank's Drug Store. Virginia and the other waitress on duty nearly collided several times as they worked quickly through the maze of tables and chairs with trays of food and pitchers to refill water, tea, and coffee.

"Miss?" An elderly man raised his arm as Virginia rushed by.

"Yes, sir?" Virginia stopped in her tracks.

"Could I please get a warm-up on my coffee?" The man held up his cup.

"I'll just get you a fresh cupful." She smiled at the man's companion across the table. "Do you need anything, ma'am, while I'm at it?"

"No, dear, I'm fine," the lady nodded and smiled. "Thank you for asking."

"Okay, I'll be back with that cup of coffee." Virginia smiled and headed for the counter.

While she poured, the cook in the back set four plates on the shelf between the counter and kitchen.

"Virginia!" he bellowed, "Your order for Table Five is up!"

Drawing in a quick breath, Virginia put the four plates on a round platter and hoisted it onto her shoulder. Turning, she grabbed the cup of coffee with her free hand and headed for the old man that had asked for the warm-up.

"Here you go, buddy," Virginia smiled as she set the cup down in front of the old man.

"Thank you, dear," he said as she sped off with the platter full of food on her shoulder.

Taking three quick steps into the main aisle toward Table Five, she happened to look toward the front door, seeing two people stepped in.

Oh my God, Dewey!

Then everything went black.

As the two of them stepped into the busy café, noisy with voices engaged in conversation, LaVonne scanned the room for a table while Neil looked for Virginia. He saw her about twenty feet in front of them, carrying her tray of food. Neil locked eyes with her and smiled. Her eyes immediately widened then filled with tears as she grew pale. Neil lurched forward when he saw her eyes roll back into her head and her knees buckle. The tray tilted backward, spilling food all over the aisle. Virginia collapsed on the floor. The entire café was startled by the scene. The other waitress ran to find the manager, while Neil knelt over Virginia as she began to recover from passing out.

"Virginia? Virginia, honey, it's Neil," he called to her softly.

Still struggling to focus, Virginia began to blink and look around.

"Virginia," Neil repeated, a little more loudly.

After a few seconds, she looked at him.

"Neil? Oh my God!" Virginia grabbed Neil's hand. "I… I thought… I thought you were Dewey walking in here."

The manager ran up from the kitchen, surveying the mess on the floor. He walked around a table full of staring people and knelt down by Virginia and Neil.

"Virginia, are you okay?" he asked, resting his hand on her shoulder.

"Yes, I'm sorry, Mr. Watson. I… I think I must have gotten a little overheated or something." She looked at him then turned and noticed the mess behind her. "I'm so sorry, that was for Table Five."

She started to get up, but Watson stopped her.

"Why don't you sit down for a bit and make sure you are okay," he said, looking around for an empty booth. Spying one, he pointed and looked at Neil. "Are you a friend of hers?"

"Yes." Neil looked at her and smiled.

"Let's get her to that booth and you can visit while she catches her breath."

"Are you sure, Mr. Watson? I know there are a lot of tables to take care of." Virginia looked around, concerned.

Watson smiled.

"I'd much rather you rest and collect yourself for a bit, to keep the food bill under control," he joked.

Virginia managed a chuckle as Neil and Watson helped her to her feet. A little wobbly, she held on to Neil as he guided her to the table, with LaVonne following closely behind.

After scooting themselves into the booth, Virginia leaned over and hugged Neil, holding on tightly.

"Oh, Neil, I've missed you," she whispered, tearing up again.

"I've missed you, too, sis," Neil whispered back.

38

October 31, 1965
Neil and LaVonne Ritter's house

The television, with the volume turned all the way down, blasted its light into the room with an old 1950s black-and-white horror movie about a giant spider invading the southwestern desert. Outside, the sun continued to sink lower on the horizon as colors shifted to orange and red. A cool breeze blew through the open window in the living room.

Neil, sitting on the couch, looked at his watch. Then he glanced at the tv, then looked out the window to the front yard, to the left, then right, then back at his watch.

"Neil, honey, you act nervous as an old cat," LaVonne chuckled from across the room. "What's the matter?"

"It's Halloween! Where are the kids?"

Just then, the sound of scampering feet hit Neil's ears and he glanced quickly outside. Then the doorbell rang.

Neil jumped up from the couch, almost running. Quickly grabbing the plastic jack-o-lantern filled with candy, he opened the door as six children crammed onto his tiny front porch and yelled "Trick or Treat!" in unison.

"Well, let's see who we have here!" Neil bellowed, almost laughing. "I see a scarecrow, a ghost! Hey, a bloody vampire! Are you a bee back there? Who else, a farmer and a monster!"

The kids giggled, eagerly holding out their buckets. Neil dropped a big candy bar in each bucket with a jovial, "And here's one for you", as each child gasped when they saw they were getting something so nice.

A chorus of "thank you" and "thank you, Mr. Ritter" sprung up from the children as they jumped off the porch and ran across the yard to the next house.

Neil turned and grinned at LaVonne.

"I think I'll just leave this door open for when the next ones show up." He chuckled as he sat down.

LaVonne sat across the room, staring at him as he craned his neck to look for more kids coming to trick-or-treat. After a moment or two of scanning the scene outside, he looked back at LaVonne and noticed the grin on her face.

"What are you grinning about?"

"You finally did it," she winked.

"Did what?"

"You finally smiled in October."

Neil smiled at her, his eyes welling up with tears.

"Yeah… I guess I did, didn't I!"

39

November 1, 1965, 2:30 a.m.
Virginia Dye's house, Ozark, Missouri

A cold wind blew outside as Virginia slept soundly, snuggled under the covers. The house was quiet, except for the occasional quiet snore coming from the children's bedroom.

"Hey, baby."

Virginia stirred.

"Hey, baby, wake up."

She took a deep breath.

"Virginia, honey, wake up."

Her eyes fluttered then opened as she felt a familiar hand gently grasp hers. She looked to her right and saw those eyes and that smile next to her.

It was Dewey.

"Oh my God, Dewey!" she whispered, trying to keep from waking the children. "Is it really you? I've missed you so badly!"

She moved forward and wrapped her arms around him as he reached around and held her tightly. With her face pressed against his neck and hair, she could smell his cologne.

"It's really me. I've missed you, too, Baby," Dewey whispered in her ear as he ran his fingers through her hair.

"Oh, Dewey, I've been trying to... trying to keep going... I've

made some mistakes... bad mistakes... but... but..."

"Shhhhhh," Dewey whispered in her ear. "It's okay, love. It's been tough, I know. But you're doing fine. You got through the tough stuff, and you did fine. And you've got two great little kids to show for it."

"They are wonderful. I love them so much."

Dewey leaned down and kissed her softly, tenderly. Tears rolled down her face as she felt his lips against hers. He wrapped his arms around her again as he continued to kiss her. It reminded Virginia of the first time they kissed as teenagers. It was soft, loving, and felt so good.

Their lips parted.

"Dewey, honey." Virginia suddenly pulled back. "I'm so sorry... I'm so sorry I didn't jump sooner. It was all my fault! If I hadn't been so scared..."

"Shhhhhhh!" Dewey put his finger up to her lips. "Baby, it wasn't your fault. The fire was too hot below us. I heard the boards creaking as I pushed you out. I knew they were going. That's why I suddenly pushed you. I didn't want all three of us to die."

"I should have stayed with you, died with you."

"No, love. If you would have died, those two beautiful little kids in the other room would never have existed. You were supposed to live. I'm just sorry I pushed you out so far, and you got hurt so bad. I didn't mean to."

"No, no, Dewey, don't apologize. I healed up okay..."

Virginia looked down at his fingers interlocked with hers.

"You know what yesterday was, Baby?" Dewey asked.

"Yes, of course. Our anniversary. We would have been married nine years." Virginia tried to smile through her tears.

"You'll always be my wife. My sweet, beautiful, loving wife."

"And you'll always be my husband. My true love."

They stared into each other's eyes for what seemed to be hours.

"Dewey... what... what about Gary?"

"Little Gary's fine, love. He's just fine. We spend all our time together. He knew I was coming to see you, so he said to tell you he loves you."

"Oh God, my baby!" Virginia fell forward into Dewey and sobbed against him. "Tell my baby that his mommy loves him so much!"

Dewey held her as she cried, stroking her hair.

"Virginia," Dewey rolled her onto her back, "Honey, I have to go..."

"No, wait! Don't go, my love!" Virginia pleaded, tears still running down her cheeks.

"No, I don't have much time. I have to go. But I wanted to see you, if only for a little while. Hold you again." Dewey smiled as he gently wiped her tears from her cheeks. "I wanted to let you know I'm okay, and that Gary's okay."

He reached out and held her face with both hands.

"And you're going to be okay, too. Everything is going to be just fine. You have to promise me that you're going to quit feeling guilty about what happened. It wasn't your fault. You have to move past that. You have to promise me that you're going to keep living, and that you'll live life to the fullest... for me and for Gary. And for those two sweet little kids. Please tell them all about me."

"Oh, Dewey. I... I promise. I'm going to shake off all this stuff and keep going. I'll tell Joy and Timmy all about you. But... but can you... can you please look in on me... from time to time?"

"Virginia, my sweet," Dewey held her hand and kissed her fingers. "I'll be watching. All you have to do is whisper my name, and I'll be right there."

"Okay my love," Virginia said, leaning forward one more time to kiss him. "I love you so much. And I miss you. Thank you for coming to see me. Happy Anniversary, Dewey."

"Happy Anniversary, Baby..."

Virginia's eyes popped open.

Oh my God! Was... was I just dreaming?

She reached down, pulled the front of her nightgown up to her nose, and took in a deep breath.

The smell of his cologne was all over her.

Dewey...

She rolled over and quietly cried herself back to sleep.

8:00 a.m.
Garland and Lula Dye's house, Ozark, Missouri

"Morning, Mom." Virginia smiled as she brought the children in for Lula to watch while she went to work.

“Good morning, dear. Come here, little girl!” Lula squatted down and held her arms out as Joy came running to her.

Virginia busied herself setting down the diaper bag and a handful of toys. After Joy finished hugging Lula and ran off to find Garland, Lula walked over to Virginia, looking intently at her face.

“Virginia? Honey? Are you okay? You have a different look on your face this morning. I can’t put my finger on it, but something is different.”

“Yes, Mom.” Virginia smiled as she held her mother’s hands. “I’m fine. I’m… I’m really, really good… For the first time in a long time, everything is… everything is fine.”

40

May 30, 1966
Ava, Missouri

"I hope I'm ready for this," Sarah whispered after a long silence.

The car quieted to a hush when they reached the city limits of Ava. Timmy squirmed in Mary's lap, tired of sitting after the 90-minute drive. Delmas, tight-lipped and gripping the wheel, said nothing as he turned left off of Highway 5 onto Springfield Road. Debbie leaned into her beloved Granny, tucked under Sarah's right arm. Next to Debbie, Doug sat up on his knees, craning his neck to see the buildings as they passed in front of him.

"Guess the ole drive-in theater will be opening soon, huh, son?" Sarah tapped Delmas on the shoulder.

"Yeah, probably so. Sure is small compared to the ones in Springfield."

"I'm sure. But little ole Ava does just fine with it," Sarah chuckled.

Delmas let out a long sigh as he turned left off of Springfield Road onto North Jefferson Street. In just a couple of blocks, they found themselves at the cemetery. The car seemed to be crawling, slowed to the 20 mile-per-hour speed limit on the road.

Sarah held Debbie close to her as the car turned into the cemetery driveway. Half-way up the hill, Delmas pulled over onto the grass and parked.

Everyone looked to their left, at the new granite headstones facing west, surrounded by bouquets and wreaths, some with fresh flowers, some adorned with plastic arrangements.

A deafening silence filled the car.

Sarah felt her heart pounding in her chest.

"Six and a half years," Sarah muttered.

"What's that, Mom?" Delmas turned toward her.

"Six and a half years. Your dad has been gone six and a half years. And now he's finally got a stone."

"All three of them do, finally," Mary said softly.

"Yes," Sarah whispered.

Sarah loosened her hold on Debbie as she opened the car door.

"Come on, Lizzie, this is what you came to do," she told herself, climbing out of the car.

Following Sarah's lead, everyone made their way out of the car and walked slowly behind her to the headstones.

"Mom," Delmas touched Sarah's arm, "Do you want us to stay back? So's you can have some time alone with them?"

"No, son," she smiled, "Please stay with me."

Debbie held Sarah's hand as they walked past Orville's stone and stopped in front of Dewey and Gary's grave. Doug, holding Delmas' hand, stood a few inches away. Mary stood nearby, keeping an eye on Timmy as he patted the top of Orville's stone while walking in circles around it.

Sarah stood quietly, staring at Dewey and Gary's gray granite headstone for several minutes without saying anything. Then with a heavy sigh, she opened her purse for a tissue as tears rolled down her face.

"It's a nice stone, son," Sarah said as she wiped her eyes.

"Yeah." Delmas quietly cleared his throat.

Sarah sat down in the grass in front of the stone and leaned in to touch the names.

"Oh my babies. Oh my poor babies." Sarah began to sob.

Debbie wrapped her arms around Sarah's neck as she cried. Doug wrapped his arms around Delmas' leg and hid behind him.

"Dear God, how he cried. He… he screamed and... and yelled as he died. There was nothing we could do. We couldn't get to him. We… we tried. We tried," Sarah cried, wrapping her arm around Debbie, who had let go of Sarah's neck and knelt down beside her.

"Who are you talking about, Granny? Why are you crying so hard? Are you hurt, Granny?" Debbie asked innocently.

"Oh, sweetheart." Sarah tried to laugh in the midst of her crying. "Has Granny scared you with all these tears?"

Debbie nodded.

"Honey, this little boy and this man died in a fire at my house several years ago."

"Your house caught fire, Granny?" Debbie's eyes widened.

"Yes, baby. It sure did. And these two died in the fire. The little boy was Gary, and he was just a little younger than your brother Timmy. And the man was my son Dewey."

"Dewey? Was he a nice man, Granny?"

"Yes, sweetheart, he was a very nice man. I hope you learn about him some day." Sarah smiled, leaning over to kiss Debbie on the forehead.

"I'm sorry you're sad, Granny," Debbie said as she hugged Sarah.

"Oh, it's okay, Debbie. Granny just has to get some tears out and then I'll be fine. Don't you worry none about your old Granny."

Sarah traced the names on the stone again then stood up with a sigh. Walking just a few feet, she stopped in front of Orville's stone. She looked over her shoulder and saw Mary sitting on the grass nearby with Timmy in her lap. She blew him a kiss then turned back around to the stone.

"I see my name is already on the stone," Sarah said quietly.

"Yeah, they said it would be easier to do that now," Delmas answered, almost whispering.

"Makes sense."

Another hush settled over the small group, interrupted only by the sound of the birds nearby and the occasional grunt from little Timmy as he shifted in his mother's lap.

Eventually Sarah spoke.

"Son, I think I'd like to take you up on that offer."

"Which offer is that, Mom?"

"I think I'd like a little alone time." Sarah turned to Delmas. "To be with Orville for a moment."

"Of course, Mom. Come on, kids, let's walk up the hill a little ways."

Mary and Tim got up as Delmas and the other two kids started up the hill to look around. Sarah sat down, crossing her legs and pulling her dress over her knees as she settled down in front of Orville's stone. She reached out and traced his name with her fingers. Tears began to roll down her cheeks again.

"Oh, Orville, honey, I hope you can hear me," she began. "Really I… I hope you're watching over me. I miss you so badly. Sometimes… sometimes at night… I lay there and think I can feel your arms around me. I… I'd give anything to feel you hold me again, Orville."

She looked down at her tissue, falling apart from being wet with tears.

"I've got my own place now, Orville. Mrs. Moody found me a nice little apartment behind Mrs. Bussard's house. I've got my own bed, and running water, and a bathroom."

She stopped to dig another tissue out of her purse.

"You're gonna laugh, honey, but… but… I can't seem to cook anything on this gas stove I have. I… I can't seem to get used to the way it heats. Everything is burned on the outside and raw on the inside."

She snickered then wiped her nose again.

"I'm all healed up now, Orville. I feel much better. The pain isn't so bad anymore. I mean, my burns don't hurt like they did. Still a little tender. But… but… I'm all healed up… on the outside anyway…"

A deep sigh.

"Oh, Orville. I miss you so bad, honey. I… I wish… I wish I could have seen you… could have talked to you, could have held your hand before you… before you left us…"

Another deep sigh.

"I wish you would have just jumped, honey. They said you might have lived if you would have just jumped. We all could have covered you up somehow… You didn't have to be so shy about it. Oh, Orville. I'm not saying any of this the way I had hoped I would…"

She sat and cried quietly for a moment.

"I'm not mad at you, dear. I just… I just miss you."

Another deep sigh.

"Orville, I've tried to be strong. I've tried to… to be a good mother… Although, I guess the kids have been taking care of me instead of the other way around. I hope you can see me. I hope… I hope that you're proud of me..."

Sarah leaned over and touched the stone and cried quietly, her tears dripping onto the gray granite. Then the emotions came boiling over, and she fell forward onto the grass, clutching at the blades, sobbing uncontrollably.

"Oh, Orville my love," was all that came out among the sobs.

After a few minutes, she exhausted herself and began to weep more quietly. She sat up again, wiping her tears and sniffling. She looked up the hill, at Delmas, Mary, and the kids, who were by this time looking back at her. She smiled and looked back down at Orville's headstone.

"I'm going to be brave, Orville. I'm going to keep living. And I'm going to teach our grandkids about you and Dewey and Gary. I'm going to teach them what a fine man you were. What a fine husband you were. And what a good grandpa you were... Orville... if you can, my love, please... please check in on me from time to time. Please... please come near me if you can. If... If you can... please let me know you are there. I love you, my dear Orville. And I always will."

With another wipe of her eyes and a quick blow of her nose, she stood up, still looking at her husband's name on the stone. Delmas and Mary began walking back down the hill, with Debbie and Doug leading the way while Timmy scampered after them.

When they got to Sarah, Doug and Debbie wrapped their arms around her neck as she knelt down to kiss them.

"Are you okay, Granny?" Doug asked.

"Yes, my sweet. Granny's fine," Sarah chuckled, kissing them both on the cheek.

"You alright, Mom?" Mary asked.

Sarah smiled.

"I'm fine dear. Thank you for giving me some time."

Delmas stood quietly looking at the stones again.

"Son, I think we should take a picture," Sarah sighed.

"I'll take it," Mary said, turning toward the car. "You guys gather 'round as you want, I'll get the camera."

After digging through the diaper bag and other sundry supplies for the kids, Mary found the camera and walked back. Delmas picked up Timmy while Sarah pulled Debbie and Doug in front of her. Mary snapped a couple of shots, making sure Orville's stone was visible, with Gary and Dewey's showing in the background.

"Thank you, dear," Sarah smiled as Mary walked toward her, "I hope those turn out good."

"I'm sure they will." Mary leaned in and kissed Sarah on the cheek.

"Let's go see if Uncle Dick is home," Delmas said while everyone piled back into the car.

As they began to drive away, Sarah turned once again to look at the stone. She put her hand on the window, a single tear running down her face.

"Bye, my love," she whispered.

She turned and pulled Debbie onto her lap, then pulled Doug closer to her.

Mary turned and looked over her shoulder from the front seat.

"Do you need anything, Mom?"

Sarah sighed.

"No, thank you, honey."

She looked back out the window at the cemetery as the car headed north.

"I think I'm gonna be just fine."

She turned back to look at Mary.

"Yep, I'm gonna be just fine."

The two women smiled at each other for a moment. Mary nodded, then turned back around.

Content, with her arms still around the children, Sarah leaned back, closed her eyes, and smiled.

EPILOGUE

Neil

Neil and LaVonne remained a strong couple, completely devoted to one another. They had three kids and raised them in Springfield. While he learned to cope with the memories of the night of The Fire which plagued him and continued to give him nightmares, every October he still withdrew into himself. According to LaVonne, the three children knew to be on their best behavior in October and were respectful of their father's mood during that time. Eventually Neil managed to forget some details of The Fire or buried them deep enough in the recesses of his mind. He always made sure Halloween was a big deal and delighted in handing out big candy bars to the kids who graced his doorstep.

To most of the nieces and nephews in the family, Neil became the favorite uncle, and he and Jack Ritter were very close. Remaining somewhat quiet throughout his adult life, he let loose with his sharp wit on many occasions, usually when it was least expected.

Sometime in the early 1990s, Neil and LaVonne and their kids were at Delmas and Mary's house. Also in attendance was Delbert and several others. Sporting a video recorder, I walked around the room capturing sights and sounds of everyone there. At one point I walked up behind Delbert as he sat at a table, deeply engrossed in a conversation about something. Neil, sitting next to him, was amused that I was filming, and more amused that Delbert had no idea. After about a minute, Neil finally leaned forward to Delbert and said, "Turn and look at the damn camera, son!"

Neil worked at the Lily Tulip manufacturing plant in Springfield for over four decades, and died suddenly in 2011, one month shy of his 71st birthday. The entire family grieved heavily over his loss.

Neil Ritter's senior year photo, taken in 1958, approximately one year before the fire.

This photo of Neil was taken in mid-1960 at Delmas and Mary's house. A mark above his right eye remains visible, and his expression indicates his continued suffering.

Neil and LaVonne's wedding photo, with Reverend Spindler behind them, August 12, 1960.

Neil and LaVonne in 2008.

Virginia

In 2004, I was working in the maintenance department at a chemical plant in Springfield. Rather than hire their own electricians, the plant contracted electrical work to a local firm, with two electricians, Jack and Tim, serving the needs of the plant five days a week. I was familiar with Jack, as we had attended the same high school. I did not know Tim prior to working at the plant, but we became good friends.

One day, Tim walked into my office and sat down next to my desk.

"What's your last name again?"

"Ritter," I answered.

"Are you related to the Ritters that lived in Ava?"

"Yes I am!"

"Are you familiar with the Ritters that lived out on the farm? They had twin sons that sang?"

"Yes, one of the twins is my dad!"

"So do you know the story about the fire?"

"Yes I sure do!"

"So you know about Dewey and Virginia and little Gary."

"Yes I do!"

"Virginia was my mother."

My jaw hit the floor. After several seconds of silence, I think I finally said, "What?"

Tim smiled and said, "Yep, Virginia was my mother. She told me all about Dewey. I've got tons of photos."

I could barely sit still, I was so blown away by this revelation. Then it hit me.

"Wait a minute. You said 'was.' Is she gone?"

"Yeah, Mom died just over two years ago."

My heart sunk.

"I'm so sorry. I always wanted to meet your mom."

From that day forward, Tim McCormack and I called each other "Cuz" and spent a lot of time talking about his mom, and what he knew about Dewey and Gary. I also learned the rest of her story.

As did her parents Garland and Lula, Virginia ended up staying in Ozark, Missouri and left waiting tables behind, getting a job at a motor assembly plant in town. She raised Joy and Tim, and eventually found love again in a wonderful man named James Watkins. But she always treasured her memories of Dewey, her first love, and little Gary.

Every Memorial Day weekend, she took Joy and Tim to the Ava City Cemetery to decorate the graves of Dewey and Gary, and those of Sarah and Orville. Later, when Tim became an adult, she asked that he promise to always decorate those graves, even after she was gone. He agreed and made metal hangers that remain at the graves to this day. Every year, he adorns the stones with red and white carnations, which were his mother's favorites.

Norman managed to keep track of Virginia and is said to have called her from time to time to check on her. When Norman died in 1982, Virginia was seen at the rear of the church during the funeral service, however left quickly after it concluded, so no one in the family got the chance to talk with her.

Virginia fought a lengthy battle with cancer and died on Christmas Day in 2001 at the age of 73.

Dewey Ritter (left) and friend outside his electronics repair business on the square in Ava, MO, c. 1956

Virginia and Dewey's wedding photo, October 31, 1956, In Ava, MO. Norman and Jerry stand with them as witnesses.

Virginia, Dewey and Gary on Gary's first birthday, May 2, 1959, in Paris, France.

Virginia and Billy Joe McCormack's blurry wedding photo, July 18, 1960. Courtesy of Joy McCroskey.

The wedding photo of Virginia's son Tim on June 25, 1983. Virginia stands on the far right.

Sarah

Sarah spent several years in the little two-bedroom apartment behind Mrs. Bussard's house on South Street in Springfield. She kept old washed-out cottage cheese containers stored in her kitchenette for her littlest grandchildren to play with during their visits and made popcorn balls for any grandchild that showed up to trick or treat on Halloween.

In late 1969, Norman purchased a small lot located across the street from his home south of Springfield and had a one-bedroom house built there. Upon its completion, he moved Sarah to the little house so that she could be closer to at least one of her children, and in a quieter location. She loved her new home and enjoyed being so close to Norman.

In late 1971, she began to have health issues, and in mid-December entered the hospital to undergo surgery to remove her gall bladder. She contracted pneumonia in the aftermath of the surgery and died on December 28, 1971. At last, she joined her beloved Orville at Ava City Cemetery.

Orville and Sarah outside the farmhouse before renovations took place, c.1950.

The last photograph taken of Orville and Sarah together.
At the farmhouse, summer 1959.

This is the snapshot that Mary took on May 30, 1966, when Sarah visited the Ava Cemetery for the first time.

Left to right: Norman, Delmas, June, Sarah, Wanda, Neil, and Ray. At a family reunion in Springfield, Missouri in 1970.

The property where the farmhouse once stood on Hunter Road outside the town of Ava changed hands many times over the years. The burned-out foundation and concrete porch stood for several years as a painful reminder of what happened on the site. Eventually it was bulldozed, the remnants of the foundation and porch sent over the edge of the original gulley (the same gulley where Virginia fell into the darkness below), to help fill the space when the owner decided to create a more gradual slope in that area. A few rocks from the farmhouse's foundation can still be found jutting out of the backfilled hillside.

At some point in the 1990s, a large new house was built further up the hill, and a cattle pen and chute erected where the farmhouse once stood. The property once again changed ownership, and the current owners extensively renovated the large house. Having been apprised of what happened on their property in 1959, they were most gracious during my visits as I performed research for this book. It is hoped that someday a little memorial may be erected where the old farmhouse once stood.

The old farmhouse in its primitive condition is visible in this photo from about 1950. Left to right: Orville, Margaret, Delbert, Sarah, and Delmas.

The farmhouse, from summer 1959. Orville and Sarah are visible sitting on the porch. One of the twins can be seen standing to the far left.

The Ritter men with their cars at the farmhouse, c.1958. Left to right, Delbert, Glen Franklin, Ray, Jack, Neil, Dick, and Orville. The upstairs window visible in this photograph is the window from which Neil, Sarah and Orville jumped the night of The Fire.

This photograph was taken upon conclusion of the graveside services for Dewey, Gary, and Orville on November 1, 1959. Dewey and Gary are in the casket to the left. Orville is in the one on the right.

About the Author

Photo by Erin Northrip, Gambles Photography

A native of Springfield, Missouri, Tim Ritter discovered writing and public speaking early in life. By age 13, he wrote two children's adventure books, several plays and created his own comic strip which eventually found its way to his junior high school newspaper. He also discovered that he liked being on stage, and how people tended to listen when he spoke into a microphone.

Throughout his professional career as a mechanical engineer, Tim wrote articles for trade magazines and was the featured speaker at hundreds of seminars across the country. However his love of the written word compelled him to continue writing poetry and short stories throughout his adult life.

Now retired, Tim lives outside Fair Grove, Missouri, with his wife, Lisa, writing full time and speaking to civic groups and organizations on a variety of topics. He is a board member of the Springfield Writers Guild and a member of the Douglas County Historical Society, Ozarks Genealogical Society, and the Poe Studies Association.

OTHER PUBLICATIONS BY TIM RITTER

Soul Sketches – 2nd Edition, released in 2020, is a heartfelt collection of short stories and poems, most of which are based on Tim's personal experiences. He refers to the book as a "real, sometimes brutal, look at life, love, marriage, divorce, and everything in between."

The Lantern series of books is a collection of lectures which have been presented to Masonic lodges in Southwest Missouri. The series has received critical acclaim from Masons across the state.

Tim can be contacted via his website at timritter.net, and can be found on Facebook at Author Tim Ritter, on Instagram at authortimritter, and Youtube at TimothyRitter.

Made in the USA
Columbia, SC
08 November 2021

48473244R00148